W9-CZK-234

Daily Quizzes
with Answer Key

Call to
FREEDOM

Beginnings to 1914

HOLT, RINEHART AND WINSTON
Harcourt Brace & Company

Austin • New York • Orlando • Atlanta • San Francisco • Boston • Dallas • Toronto • London

Cover: Christie's Images

Copyright © by Holt, Rinehart and Winston

Printed in the United States of America

ISBN 0-03-054502-1

4 5 6 7 8 9   085   01

★ DAILY QUIZZES ★

CHAPTER 1

The World Before the Opening of the Atlantic

★ ★

DAILY QUIZ 1.1

MULTIPLE CHOICE *10 points each*   For each of the following, write the letter of the *best* choice in the space provided.

_____ **1.** The Adena and Hopewell cultures are well known for their
  a. pit houses.
  b. extensive burial mounds.
  c. advanced form of glyph writing.
  d. temple pyramids and palaces.

_____ **2.** Which of the following is an early stone spear point that has been found throughout North America?
  a. the Folsom
  b. the Tenochtitlán
  c. the Clovis
  d. the Beringia

_____ **3.** The Anasazi built pueblos on mesas and into cliffsides
  a. because they were almost completely surrounded by water.
  b. as a means of defense against possible invasion.
  c. as a place to bury honored individuals along with their wealth.
  d. because they learned this building technique from the Toltec.

_____ **4.** The Mesoamerican civilization that has been called the Mother Culture of later civilizations is the
  a. Aztec.
  b. Olmec.
  c. Maya.
  d. Toltec.

_____ **5.** Inca armies and messengers could move quickly throughout their empire because the Inca
  a. created a vast road network.
  b. were accomplished horseback riders.
  c. built their central city in the middle of a large lake.
  d. controlled only a small area of land.

_____ **6.** By conquering most of the groups living in central Mexico, the Aztec were able to
  a. migrate to present-day Canada.
  b. do away with the practice of building mounds for defense.
  c. maintain a large trading network.
  d. influence the development of Olmec culture.

_____ **7.** The development of agriculture in the southwestern region of North America was important because
  a. all of the small mammals formerly hunted for food had died out.
  b. farmers melted the glaciers, thus creating more land to farm.
  c. it encouraged the creation of permanent settlements.
  d. it was the only way the Maya could feed all the people in their empire.

_____ **8.** What was the most useful crop grown by Native Americans in North America and Mesoamerica?
  a. maize
  b. potatoes
  c. broccoli
  d. lettuce

_____ **9.** Most historians believe that the Paleo-Indians came to North America from
  a. South America in wooden dugouts.
  b. Africa across the Atlantic Ocean.
  c. Mesoamerica to escape a drought.
  d. Asia to Alaska across a land bridge.

_____ **10.** The Mississippi culture revolved around
  a. continuous migration.
  b. the making of gold and silver jewelry.
  c. hunting and gathering.
  d. religious practices honoring the dead.

The World Before the Opening of the Atlantic

★ ★

DAILY QUIZ 1.2

FILL IN THE BLANK *10 points each*   For each of the following statements, fill in the blank with the appropriate word, phrase, or name.

1. The cultural developments of the various Native American groups living in North America reflected the unique _____ in which they lived.

2. The Inuit and the _____ who lived in the Arctic region used dogsleds and kayaks for transportation.

3. Native Americans who lived in the Subarctic region of North America formed small groups, called _____ , to fish and to gather wild plants.

4. Individuals in Northwest culture groups demonstrated their wealth and earned high social standing by holding _____ , events at which hosts gave away most of their goods in order to gain respect.

5. The main food of _____ culture groups was acorns, which they ground into a coarse flour.

6. Because the Great Basin is primarily _____ , the Native Americans who lived there had to constantly move in search of food.

7. The religious ceremonies, rituals, and festivals of the Pueblo culture group revolved around the two life-giving forces of Pueblo existence—rain and _____ .

8. Pawnee society was matrilineal, which means that members of the Pawnee culture group identified themselves by tracing their ancestry through their _____ .

9. Some Algonquian peoples who lived in the warmer areas of the Northeast created permanent villages and built a variety of housing structures, such as large multifamily lodges and small _____ , or circular huts.

10. The _____ was the only Native American culture group controlled economically by women.

CHAPTER 1

Name _____ Class _____ Date _____

The World Before the Opening of the Atlantic

★ ★ ★ ★ ★ ★ ★ ★ ★ ★ ★ ★ ★ ★ ★ ★ ★ ★ ★ ★

DAILY QUIZ 1.3

MATCHING *10 points each*   Match each of the following people or terms with the correct description by writing the letter of the description in the space provided. Some descriptions will not be used.

_____ **1.** Vikings

_____ **2.** peasants

_____ **3.** King William of Normandy

_____ **4.** feudalism

_____ **5.** King John

_____ **6.** Leif Eriksson

_____ **7.** nobles

_____ **8.** Middle Ages

_____ **9.** Magna Carta

_____ **10.** monasteries

a. people during the Middle Ages who farmed the land on manors

b. religious centers that provided homes for elderly and unmarried noblewomen

c. adventurer who sailed to North America and established what was to be a short-lived colony called Vinland

d. people during the Middle Ages who defended their kingdoms and manors with the help of loyal vassals

e. Great Charter, signed in 1215, that made it clear that even monarchs must observe the law

f. seafaring Scandinavian people whose unique ship-building design allowed them to explore new lands and establish new colonies

g. large estates that were a vital part of the feudal system

h. system of government in which people pledge loyalty to a lord in exchange for protection

i. monarch who was forced to sign the Magna Carta by nobles rebelling against the misuse of royal power

j. isolated religious communities that became centers of education and book production

k. historical time period that began with the collapse of the Roman Empire

l. monarch whose survey of his realm resulted in the Domesday Book, which helped the monarch establish taxes and distribute land fairly

CHAPTER
1

The World Before the Opening of the Atlantic

★ ★

DAILY QUIZ 1.4

TRUE/FALSE *10 points each*   Indicate whether each statement below is true or false by writing *T* or *F* in the space provided. If the statement is false, explain why.

_____**1.** The holy book of Islam is the Qur'an.

_____

_____**2.** Muslim trade networks helped spread Islam and brought new ideas to Muslim scholars.

_____

_____**3.** At the urging of the pope, Christians joined the Crusades in order to retake Jerusalem.

_____

_____**4.** After gaining control of China, Mongol leader Genghis Khan opened trading networks.

_____

_____**5.** The Ming dynasty abandoned international trade in the mid-1400s due to political conflicts, a lack of tax money, and other events.

_____

_____**6.** The city-states of East Africa first began as market centers for Bantu and Arab traders.

_____

_____**7.** Because the kingdoms of West Africa wished to remain isolated from outside influences, they refused to participate in trading networks.

_____

_____**8.** Most of Ghana's wealth came from trading camels and other livestock.

_____

_____**9.** The Berbers were the first people to use camels to carry goods across the desert.

_____

_____**10.** While on a pilgrimage to the Islamic holy city of Mecca, Mali leader Mansa Musa impressed Arabs with his wealth and power.

_____

Name _____ Class _____ Date _____

The Age of Exploration

★ ★

DAILY QUIZ 2.1

MATCHING *10 points each*   Match each of the following people or terms with the correct description by writing the letter of the description in the space provided. Some descriptions will not be used.

_____**1.** Black Death   _____**6.** Renaissance

_____ **2.** Commercial Revolution   _____**7.** astrolabe

_____ **3.** capital   _____**8.** printing press

_____ **4.** Michelangelo Buonarroti   _____**9.** Leonardo da Vinci

_____ **5.** joint-stock company   _____**10.** caravel

a. rebirth of European interest in the arts and learning of ancient Greece and Rome

b. business in which a group of people jointly invest and share in the profits and losses

c. epidemic that from 1348 to about 1350 killed about one third of Europe's population

d. person who started a school in Sagres, Portugal, and gathered together the finest mapmakers, sailors, and shipbuilders

e. money or property that is used to earn more money

f. painter of the *Mona Lisa* who also studied such subjects as architecture, astronomy, biology, geology, and machinery

g. small ship built to be very maneuverable and fast

h. period of economic development that brought dramatic changes in the way merchants conducted business

i. invention by Johannes Gutenberg that helped spread the science and literature of the Renaissance throughout Europe

j. name given to the southern tip of Africa by explorer Bartholomeu Dias

k. creator of the sculpture *David* who painted the artwork on the ceiling of the Sistine Chapel in the Vatican

l. instrument used to determine a ship's position by charting the position of the stars

FILL IN THE BLANK *10 points each*   For each of the following statements, fill in the blank with the appropriate word, phrase, or name.

1. Christopher Columbus was convinced that he could reach _____ by sailing west across the Atlantic Ocean.

2. The conquest of Granada by the Spanish ended the _____ , a centuries-long struggle to drive the Moors out of Spain.

3. In exchange for funding, Christopher Columbus promised Spain's rulers that he would claim for Spain any lands he explored and that he would try to _____ any native peoples he encountered to Christianity.

4. The three ships that made up Christopher Columbus's first fleet were the *Niña,* the *Pinta,* and the _____ .

5. The people that Christopher Columbus encountered on the island he called Hispaniola were the _____ , not the Chinese or Japanese people he expected to find.

6. By creating the _____ , Pope Alexander VI set the boundary of Spain's exploration and monopoly rights.

7. The Treaty of _____ gave Portugal more opportunity to claim lands unexplored by other Europeans.

8. When Christopher Columbus, on his second voyage, returned to the colony he had named _____ , he found that the colony had been destroyed and that all of his sailors had been killed.

9. On Columbus's third voyage he became the first European to see_____ , which he wrote in his journal was like paradise on Earth.

10. Against the wishes of Queen Isabella, Christopher Columbus allowed the European settlers to enslave _____ .

TRUE/FALSE *10 points each* Indicate whether each statement below is true or false by writing *T* or *F* in the space provided. If the statement is false, explain why.

_____ **1.** King Manuel of Portugal chose Christopher Columbus to command another expedition around the Cape of Good Hope.

_____

_____ **2.** The fleet of Pedro Alvares Cabral was blown far off course and eventually landed somewhere along the coast of present-day Alaska.

_____

_____ **3.** The voyage of John Cabot gave France a claim to land in North America.

_____

_____ **4.** North and South America were named in honor of the explorer Amerigo Vespucci.

_____

_____ **5.** Balboa named the great blue sea he found on his expedition the Southern Ocean.

_____

_____ **6.** Although Ferdinand Magellan was Portuguese, he received funding from England to make a voyage west in search of Asia.

_____

_____ **7.** The passageway that Magellan's ships found at the southern tip of South America became known as the Strait of Magellan.

_____

_____ **8.** Magellan's crew renamed the ocean found by Balboa the Pacific Ocean.

_____

_____ **9.** All three of Magellan's ships were able to make their way back to Spain.

_____

_____ **10.** Magellan's crew circumnavigated the globe and gave Spain an all-water route to China.

_____

Name _____ Class _____ Date _____

The Age of Exploration

★ ★

DAILY QUIZ 2.4

MULTIPLE CHOICE *10 points each*   For each of the following, write the letter of the *best* choice in the space provided.

_____ **1.** A river near the island of Manhattan was named in honor of the explorer
   a. Amerigo Vespucci.
   b. Henry Hudson.
   c. Ferdinand Magellan.
   d. Jacques Cartier.

_____ **2.** Which of the following American Indian crops did explorers bring back to Europe?
   a. wheat
   b. rice
   c. corn
   d. barley

_____ **3.** Many American Indians died because
   a. their digestive systems could not tolerate European foods.
   b. they were allergic to European tobacco.
   c. they were thrown off European ships and could not swim.
   d. they had no immunity to European diseases.

_____ **4.** Why did European nations want to find the Northwest Passage?
   a. They hoped it would allow them to sail from the Atlantic to the Pacific.
   b. It was believed to contain huge quantities of gold.
   c. The nation that found it would be able to lay claim to all of South America.
   d. It contained spices and textiles to rival those of China.

_____ **5.** Which of the following explorers was able to find the Northwest Passage?
   a. Henry Hudson
   b. Jacques Cartier
   c. Giovanni da Verrazzano
   d. None of the above

_____ **6.** The voyages of Samuel de Champlain became the basis of French claims to much of
   a. Canada.
   b. California.
   c. Brazil.
   d. Louisiana.

_____ **7.** During the 1500s as much as 75 percent of the spice trade between Europe and Asia was controlled by
   a. Italy.
   b. Portugal.
   c. England.
   d. Spain.

_____ **8.** Which of the following people explored North America for both the Dutch and the English?
   a. Ferdinand Magellan
   b. Samuel de Champlain
   c. Giovanni da Verrazzano
   d. Henry Hudson

_____ **9.** The Columbian Exchange refers to
   a. the transfer of plants, animals, and diseases between Europe, Asia, and Africa and the Americas.
   b. a European banking system named in honor of Christopher Columbus.
   c. the promises made by Christopher Columbus to Spanish rulers in exchange for funding.
   d. the water passageway through South America to the Pacific Ocean.

_____ **10.** Which explorer sailed from the St. Lawrence River to present-day Montreal?
   a. Giovanni da Verrazzano
   b. John Cabot
   c. Jacques Cartier
   d. Henry Hudson

UNIT 1

★ ★

GEOGRAPHY AND HISTORY QUIZ

The Columbian Exchange

FILL IN THE BLANK *10 points each*   For each of the following statements, fill in the blank with the appropriate word, phrase, or name.

1. The Columbian Exchange began as explorers brought plants and animals from Europe, Africa, and _____ along with them on their voyages to the Americas.

2. The _____ Hemisphere contributed a wider variety of food crops to the other hemisphere.

3. The _____ today accounts for more than half of all the income the United States earns from animal products.

4. During the 1500s, most Europeans fed _____ to their livestock rather than eat it themselves.

5. At one time the _____ , which was originally grown in the Americas, was the main crop of Ireland.

6. The French became famous for their chocolate, which is made from _____ beans that originated in the Americas.

7. Rice originated on the continent of _____ .

8. Until the 1800s, Europeans did not eat American _____ because they believed them to be poisonous.

9. American Indians of the western _____ learned to train and ride horses in the 1600s and made them a part of their culture.

10. One example of how the Columbian Exchange continues to the present day is the Africanized _____ , which today can be found in both Texas and California.

New Empires in the Americas

★ ★

DAILY QUIZ 3.1

TRUE/FALSE *10 points each*   Indicate whether each statement below is true or false by writing *T* or *F* in the space provided. If the statement is false, explain why.

_____ **1.** The conquistadores were Spanish soldiers and explorers who led military expeditions in the Americas.

_____

_____ **2.** Attacks by Cortés and diseases brought by the Spanish led to the fall of the Aztec.

_____

_____ **3.** When Atahuallpa delivered to Pizarro the agreed ransom, Pizarro freed the ruler.

_____

_____ **4.** Ponce de León searched for gold and the Fountain of Youth in a land he named Georgia.

_____

_____ **5.** Survivors of the ill-fated Narváez expedition included Cabeza de Vaca and Estevanico.

_____

_____ **6.** Hernando de Soto was the first European to cross the Mississippi River.

_____

_____ **7.** When Francisco Vásquez de Coronado reached Cíbola, he found that it was full of gold.

_____

_____ **8.** Among the Indians that Coronado encountered in his travels were the Zuni and the Hopi.

_____

_____ **9.** Juan Rodríquez Cabrillo sailed up the coast of present-day California hoping to find gold or a new sea route to China.

_____

_____ **10.** Cabrillo's voyage established a Spanish claim to the Pacific coast of North America.

_____

MATCHING *10 points each*   Match each of the following people or terms with the correct description by writing the letter of the description in the space provided. Some descriptions will not be used.

_____**1.** pueblos

_____**2.** missions

_____**3.** presidios

_____**4.** *encomienda* system

_____**5.** Bartolomé de Las Casas

_____**6.** plantations

_____**7.** Pedro Menéndez de Avilés

_____**8.** El Camino Real

_____**9.** *peninsulares*

_____**10.** *mestizos*

a. military bases built in New Spain to protect existing towns and missions

b. people living in New Spain who had Spanish parents but were born in the Americas

c. person who destroyed a French town and established the fort of St. Augustine in eastern Florida

d. towns in New Spain that served as trading posts and sometimes as centers of local government

e. *encomendero* who later became a Catholic priest and worked to protect the rights of American Indians

f. Spanish missionary who oversaw the building of nine missions along the California coast

g. settlements in New Spain established by priests for the purpose of converting local Indians to Catholicism

h. people living in New Spain who were born to Spanish and Indian parents

i. road built by Spanish settlers to connect communities in New Spain

j. system established by Spain that gave settlers the right to tax local Indians or to demand labor from them in exchange for the settlers' protection

k. white Spaniards born in Spain who held the most important political offices in Spanish America

l. large farms in New Spain that usually specialized in growing one kind of crop, such as sugar

MULTIPLE CHOICE *10 points each* For each of the following, write the letter of the *best* choice in the space provided.

_____ **1.** The people who wished to reform the Catholic Church became known as
  a. Jehovah's Witnesses.
  b. Protestants.
  c. Muslims.
  d. Mormons.

_____ **2.** Which of the following inventions played an important role in expressing and spreading the ideas of the Reformation?
  a. astrolabe
  b. radio
  c. telegraph
  d. printing press

_____ **3.** One complaint that supporters of the Reformation had about the Catholic Church was that
  a. the pope possessed too much power.
  b. priests did not have the right to interpret the Bible.
  c. it contained too many Protestants.
  d. the Bible described a complex religion and the practices of the Catholic Church were too simplistic.

_____ **4.** By making himself the head of the Anglican Church, King Henry VIII
  a. became the new Catholic pope.
  b. outlawed the Protestant religion.
  c. banned Catholicism in England.
  d. defied the authority of the pope.

_____ **5.** The Spanish Armada was a
  a. sculpture created by Spain's most famous artist.
  b. series of forts built in New Spain to protect settlers against Indian attack.
  c. huge fleet of ships that Philip II intended to use to overthrow Queen Elizabeth and the Anglican Church.
  d. nickname given to Spain's most successful sea captain.

_____ **6.** Who were the sea dogs?
  a. American Indians who used dugout canoes to raid English settlements
  b. English sailors who raided Spanish treasure ships
  c. Dutch pirates who tried to eliminate Native Americans living in Florida
  d. Portuguese merchants who controlled European trade with Asia

_____ **7.** What was the outcome of the sea battles between England and Spain?
  a. The Spanish fleet was defeated.
  b. An unexpected French fleet defeated both England and Spain.
  c. The English fleet was defeated.
  d. England and Spain signed a truce giving neither side a victory.

_____ **8.** Which of the following people wrote *Don Quixote,* a novel that made fun of European knights?
  a. El Greco
  b. Sir Francis Drake
  c. Miguel de Cervantes
  d. Lope de Vega

_____ **9.** The large amounts of silver that Spain received from the Americas caused
  a. the Counter Reformation.
  b. inflation in Spain.
  c. fighting between Catholics and Protestants.
  d. the overthrow of Queen Elizabeth by Spanish forces.

_____ **10.** A priest named Martin Luther
  a. became the most successful of the sea dogs.
  b. led the Counter Reformation.
  c. became the most celebrated pope in history.
  d. started the Reformation.

FILL IN THE BLANK *10 points each*   For each of the following statements, fill in the blank with the appropriate word, phrase, or name.

1. In 1565 French Huguenots established a few small colonies in _____ , but they were soon driven out by the Spanish.

2. The explorations of Samuel de Champlain and Jacques Cartier gave France a claim to much of present-day eastern _____ .

3. In the Great Lakes region of North America, the French traded tools, jewelry, and cloth with local Indians in exchange for _____ , which they then shipped back to France.

4. The explorer Rene-Robert de _____ named the Mississippi Valley region Louisiana and claimed it for France.

5. Peter Minuit purchased _____ from a local Indian tribe and founded the settlement of New Amsterdam.

6. The religious toleration of the _____ helped make New Amsterdam appealing to settlers from many different countries.

7. _____ settlers, who established their colony along the Delaware River, were among the first people in North America to build log cabins.

8. The colony that Sir _____ founded on Roanoke Island failed, and Sir Francis Drake took the settlers home to England.

9. _____ was the first English child born in the present-day United States.

10. When John White returned to the deserted Roanoke Island in 1590, he found carved into a post the word *CROTOAN*, which may have been the name of a nearby island inhabited by _____ .

★ ★

DAILY QUIZ 4.1

MATCHING *10 points each* Match each of the following people or terms with the correct description by writing the letter of the description in the space provided. Some descriptions will not be used.

_____ **1.** John Smith

_____ **2.** Powhatan Confederacy

_____ **3.** John Rolfe

_____ **4.** Pocahontas

_____ **5.** headright system

_____ **6.** indentured servants

_____ **7.** Africans

_____ **8.** House of Burgesses

_____ **9.** William Berkeley

_____ **10.** Bacon's Rebellion

a. attack on some friendly American Indians by a wealthy relative of the governor, along with a group of slaves, freed slaves, and former servants

b. Jamestown colonist who in 1612 introduced a new variety of tobacco, which the colonists were able to export to England

c. Powhatan who sent a warning and later attacked the colonists on the morning of Good Friday in 1622

d. governor of Virginia who complained about the large number of poor and discontented colonists

e. system in which each colonist who paid his or her own way to Virginia received 50 acres of land plus 50 more acres for every additional person brought from England

f. Virginia's elected assembly, whose members were accused by poor colonists of raising taxes only to pay themselves higher salaries

g. person whose failed Roanoke colony led the London Company to take a different approach to settlement

h. person who gained control of Jamestown in 1608 and forced the settlers to plant crops and build better housing

i. powerful alliance of Algonquian Indians under the leadership of Wahunsonacock

j. people who first arrived in Virginia on board a Dutch ship in 1619

k. people who signed a contract to work from four to seven years for those who paid their ship fare to America

l. person who helped achieve more peaceful relations between the colonists and the Powhatans for a time by marrying John Rolfe

TRUE/FALSE *10 points each*   Indicate whether each statement below is true or false by writing *T* or *F* in the space provided. If the statement is false, explain why.

_____ **1.** A group in England called the Puritans wanted to reform the Catholic Church.

_____

_____ **2.** Separatists developed their own churches and cut all ties with the Church of England.

_____

_____ **3.** The Pilgrims moved to America to escape religious persecution in the Netherlands.

_____

_____ **4.** The Mayflower Compact was a legal contract signed by the male passengers aboard the *Mayflower* establishing basic laws and social rules to govern their new colony.

_____

_____ **5.** Squanto taught the settlers how to plant corn and fertilize the soil and where to catch fish.

_____

_____ **6.** To celebrate the harvest of their first crops, the Pilgrims invited the Pawtuxet Indians to what became known as the first Thanksgiving.

_____

_____ **7.** Back in England, the non-Pilgrim merchants who had invested in the Plymouth colony were thrilled by the colony's fast economic growth.

_____

_____ **8.** Pilgrim families served as centers of faith, health care, and community well-being.

_____

_____ **9.** Pilgrims wanted large families because children were needed to help with the work.

_____

_____ **10.** Women in Plymouth had fewer rights than women had in England.

_____

Name _____ Class _____ Date _____

FILL IN THE BLANK *10 points each*   For each of the following statements, fill in the blank with the appropriate word, phrase, or name.

1. In 1629 William Laud, head of the Church of England, began to make life difficult for the Puritans because they were _____ , people who disagree with official religious or political opinions.

2. During the _____ , which occurred between 1629 and 1640, at least 80,000 English men, women, and children left England.

3. The Puritan colonists who left England for Massachusetts hoped they would have the freedom there to establish their own _____ .

4. The focus of local New England politics was the _____ , in which a settlement discussed and decided issues of local interest, such as local regulations and the support of schools.

5. Farmers in New England concentrated their efforts on growing _____ rather than crops such as tobacco, which was unsuitable for the New England climate.

6. Parents in colonial New England helped choose their children's marriage partners, in part because marriage involved a transfer of _____ from one family to another.

7. The first law regulating education in Massachusetts was passed in 1647, in part because New Englanders wanted their children to be able to read the _____ .

8. After Roger Williams was forced to leave Massachusetts for criticizing Puritan officials, he and his supporters established a settlement called _____ , which later became the New England colony of Rhode Island.

9. _____ angered Massachusetts authorities by publicly discussing what they considered to be radical religious ideas, so they put her on trial for her beliefs.

10. The largest number of witchcraft trials occurred in _____ , Massachusetts, when the local doctors suspected witchcraft after the daughter and niece of the town's minister began suffering from fits.

Name _____ Class _____ Date _____

MULTIPLE CHOICE *10 points each* For each of the following, write the letter of the *best* choice in the space provided.

_____ **1.** The first law in America protecting religious freedom was passed in
  a. South Carolina.
  b. New York.
  c. Georgia.
  d. Maryland.

_____ **2.** Which of the following colonies offered settlers generous amounts of land, religious freedom, security from government abuses, and benefits such as government care for the poor?
  a. Pennsylvania
  b. New Netherland
  c. North Carolina
  d. South Carolina

_____ **3.** Colonists who paid their own way to South Carolina received
  a. free education for their children.
  b. judgeships in local courts.
  c. grants of land.
  d. free crop seeds and planting tools.

_____ **4.** Which of the following had the highest slave population in the colonies?
  a. New Jersey
  b. Georgia
  c. Maryland
  d. South Carolina

_____ **5.** In 1664 the English took control of New Netherland's territory away from
  a. the French.
  b. the Dutch.
  c. the Spanish.
  d. the Swedes.

_____ **6.** When the English took over New Netherland, they renamed it
  a. New Hampshire.
  b. New England.
  c. New York.
  d. New Jersey.

_____ **7.** The Duke of York made Sir George Carteret and Lord John Berkeley the proprietors of
  a. Maryland.
  b. New York.
  c. Georgia.
  d. New Jersey.

_____ **8.** Which of the following pairs of colonies was originally established as a single colony?
  a. North Carolina and South Carolina
  b. Florida and Georgia
  c. New York and New Jersey
  d. Pennsylvania and New Hampshire

_____ **9.** William Penn built the capital of his colony in a city he named
  a. Boston.
  b. Philadelphia.
  c. Charleston.
  d. Princeton.

_____ **10.** Georgia was originally established by charter as a colony for English citizens who
  a. desired religious freedom.
  b. had been jailed for debt.
  c. did not own land in England.
  d. wanted to own slaves.

Life in the English Colonies

★ ★

DAILY QUIZ 5.1

TRUE/FALSE *10 points each* Indicate whether each statement below is true or false by writing *T* or *F* in the space provided. If the statement is false, explain why.

_____**1.** When founded, each of the original thirteen English colonies had established its own form of government and had operated independently of one another.

_____

_____**2.** The colonies fell into four categories: proprietary, company, independent, and royal.

_____

_____**3.** A group of royal advisers called the Royal Council set policy for the thirteen colonies.

_____

_____**4.** Each of the thirteen colonies had a governor, who served as head of the colony's government.

_____

_____**5.** Some colonies elected representatives to an assembly that was modeled on the English Parliament's one-house legislature.

_____

_____**6.** The New England colonies developed a tradition of holding yearly town meetings.

_____

_____**7.** The case of John Peter Zenger established colonists' right to freedom of religion.

_____

_____**8.** In 1686 James II united the New England colonies under the Dominion of New England.

_____

_____**9.** The overthrow of James II by the rulers of the Netherlands became known as the Fabulous Rebellion.

_____

_____**10.** The English monarchy's powers increased greatly during the reign of William and Mary.

_____

Life in the English Colonies

★ ★

DAILY QUIZ 5.2

FILL IN THE BLANK *10 points each*   For each of the following statements, fill in the blank with the appropriate word, phrase, or name.

1. In the late 1600s most nations in western Europe organized their economies around the practice

of _____ , creating and maintaining wealth by carefully controlling trade.

2. The goal of English officials was to create profits for their country by establishing a favorable

_____ by decreasing their imports and increasing their exports.

3. Between 1650 and 1696 Parliament passed a series of _____ Acts to regulate

trade with the colonies and to increase profits for England.

4. The 1707 Act of Union between England and _____ created the United

Kingdom of Great Britain and expanded English power.

5. The term _____ refers to the movement of goods from the colonies to the

West Indies to Britain.

6. The voyage involving the transport of Africans across the Atlantic Ocean to be sold as slaves in

North and South America and the West Indies was called the _____ .

7. Slave traders fit as many captured Africans as possible on board their ships in order to increase

_____ .

8. Thousands of captive Africans died during the voyage across the Atlantic Ocean either from

_____ or from being thrown overboard when they became ill.

9. In 1688 _____ in Germantown, Pennsylvania, made the first recorded

colonial protest against the practice of slavery.

10. _____ , a Massachusetts merchant and judge, published a pamphlet in 1700

arguing against slavery.

Name _____ Class _____ Date _____

Life in the English Colonies

★ ★

DAILY QUIZ 5.3

MULTIPLE CHOICE *10 points each*   For each of the following, write the letter of the *best* choice in the space provided.

_____ **1.** For the most part, the southern colonies based their economy on the production of
  a. cash crops.
  b. precious minerals.
  c. timber.
  d. staple crops.

_____ **2.** Two of the leading industries in New England were
  a. cattle ranching and mining.
  b. slave trading and textiles.
  c. shoemaking and the manufacture of weapons.
  d. fishing and shipbuilding.

_____ **3.** By the 1700s the main labor force in the South was made up of
  a. American Indians.
  b. plantation owners and their families.
  c. indentured servants.
  d. enslaved Africans.

_____ **4.** Why did most of the southern colonies pass slave codes?
  a. to provide ways by which slaves could buy their freedom
  b. to control slaves and limit their freedom
  c. to limit to four the number of years of schooling available to slaves
  d. to provide a language that was to be used only by slaves

_____ **5.** The staple crops produced in the middle colonies included
  a. cotton and silk.
  b. wheat, barley, and oats.
  c. potatoes, yams, and corn.
  d. apples, peaches, pears, and plums.

_____ **6.** Indigo was introduced in the South by
  a. William Byrd II.
  b. Gabriel Ginings.
  c. Eliza Lucas Pinckney.
  d. Robert Beverley.

_____ **7.** Whaling was common in the
  a. southern colonies.
  b. middle colonies.
  c. New England colonies.
  d. all of the above.

_____ **8.** Young boys who were sent off from their families to learn skilled trades were known as
  a. indigo boys.
  b. apprentices.
  c. indentured servants.
  d. master craftsmen.

_____ **9.** Which of the following describes the New England agricultural environment?
  a. The climate was harsh, the soil was rocky, and the few rivers were unsuitable for navigation.
  b. The climate was warm and the growing season was long.
  c. There was plenty of fertile land and the growing season was good.
  d. The almost desert-like heat and drought made it difficult to grow any crops other than wheat and cotton.

_____ **10.** Throughout the colonies, women were more likely than men to work as
  a. farmers and ranchers.
  b. tailors, barbers, and saloonkeepers.
  c. doctors, nurses, and midwives.
  d. fishers, hunters, and whalers.

Name _____ Class _____ Date _____

Life in the English Colonies

★ ★

DAILY QUIZ 5.4

FILL IN THE BLANK *10 points each* For each of the following statements, fill in the blank with the appropriate word, phrase, or name.

1. To renew the declining enthusiasm for religion, ministers in the late 1730s began holding _____ , often in open fields.

2. Historians use the term _____ to describe the unorganized but widespread movement of evangelical Christian sermons and church meetings in the 1730s and 1740s.

3. Two of the most important leaders of the religious revival were _____ and George Whitefield.

4. The ministers of the religious revival preached that all people, regardless of their social status, were born _____ , but that everyone had an equal chance to be saved.

5. In New England, followers of the religious revival were called "_____ ," while traditionalists were called "_____ ."

6. In the middle colonies, the _____ Church split into two groups, with the "Old Sides" opposing the religious revival and the "New Sides" following the preachings of minister Gilbert Tennent.

7. Because there were few established churches on the frontier, the message of the religious revival was brought to western settlers by _____ preachers, or preachers who traveled the country delivering sermons.

8. Many women sought spiritual renewel around the time of _____ , when their lives often were at risk.

9. Despite the message of acceptance and spiritual equality preached by the ministers of the religious revival, most revivals were separated by _____ .

10. Some historians believe that the questioning of traditional church practices common during the time of the religious revival may have eventually encouraged colonists to demand greater _____ equality.

MATCHING *10 points each*   Match each of the following people or terms with the correct description by writing the letter of the description in the space provided. Some descriptions will not be used.

_____**1.** Scientific Revolution

_____**2.** Galileo Galilei

_____**3.** Sir Isaac Newton

_____**4.** scientific method

_____**5.** Enlightenment

_____**6.** John Locke

_____**7.** David Rittenhouse

_____**8.** Benjamin Banneker

_____**9.** Benjamin Franklin

_____**10.** Anne Bradstreet

a. process in which a person carefully examines natural events and then forms theories from experiments and observations

b. Enlightenment philosopher who argued that in the social contract, people voluntarily obey their rulers only when the state fulfills its responsibility to protect people's life, liberty, and property

c. person who in 1767 constructed the most accurate orrery, a model displaying the planetary system, produced up to that time in the colonies

d. leading figure of the Scientific Revolution who confirmed Copernicus's theory that the planets revolve around the sun

e. first college founded in the English colonies

f. historical era that began in the 1600s, in which western Europeans began to search for new information about the fundamental laws that govern nature and the universe

g. New England poet whose book *The Tenth Muse* reflected her love for her family and her dedication to her faith

h. first colonial organization with a mission to study science

i. person who founded the first circulating library in the colonies and who invented the lightning rod, a type of stove, and bifocal eyeglasses

j. scientist whose writings became the foundation for physics for the next 200 years and formed the basis for the methods scientists use today

k. free African American who included his astronomical calculations and his comments on social problems in an almanac that he wrote and published yearly

l. Age of Reason, in which thinkers applied reason and logic to the study of human nature and the improvement of society

★ ★

GEOGRAPHY AND HISTORY QUIZ

Colonial Economies

MATCHING *10 points each*   Match each of the following items with its correct description by writing the letter of the description in the space provided. Some descriptions will not be used.

_____ **1.** American Indians

_____ **2.** West Indies

_____ **3.** enslaved Africans

_____ **4.** rice

_____ **5.** Britain

_____ **6.** Africa

_____ **7.** fur

_____ **8.** France

_____ **9.** Brazil

_____ **10.** tobacco

   a. place that was first among the destinations for U.S. exports in 1995

   b. important food crop in the southern colonies

   c. nation that banned the importing of slaves in 1807

   d. people who were important partners with French colonists in the fur trade

   e. place that in recent years has ranked only fourth as a destination for exports from the United States

   f. people who cleared land, put up buildings, and tended crops on southern plantations

   g. British colonial export whose total value varied from year to year, depending on whether British relations with American Indians and the French were friendly or hostile

   h. important destination for goods shipped from the British colonies

   i. Atlantic slave trade destination that received the largest percentage of slaves between 1701 and 1760

   j. colonial crop that was used by American Indians for ceremonial purposes long before Europeans arrived in the Americas

   k. nation whose explorers used light Indian canoes to travel the inland waterways of North America, allowing them to dominate trade in the region west of the Appalachian Mountains

   l. destination that received the smallest percentage of the value of colonial exports

CHAPTER 6

Name _____ Class _____ Date _____

Conflicts in the Colonies

★ ★

DAILY QUIZ 6.1

TRUE/FALSE *10 points each* Indicate whether each statement below is true or false by writing *T* or *F* in the space provided. If the statement is false, explain why.

_____ **1.** King Philip's War was unusual in that no deaths occurred on either side.

_____

_____ **2.** The French were able to maintain the trust of Indian allies because the small French settlements were seen as less threatening than the fast-growing English colonies.

_____

_____ **3.** In the treaty that ended Queen Anne's War, England received present-day Newfoundland, Nova Scotia, and Hudson Bay from France.

_____

_____ **4.** The Albany Plan of Union was approved by all of the colonial governments.

_____

_____ **5.** The battle at Fort Necessity was the last battle of the French and Indian War.

_____

_____ **6.** The traditional military tactics used by General Edward Braddock's troops against the French and American Indians led to high numbers of British casualties.

_____

_____ **7.** In 1758 the British captured Fort Duquesne and renamed it Fort Pitt.

_____

_____ **8.** The French capture of Quebec was a turning point of the war.

_____

_____ **9.** The Treaty of Paris officially ended the war between the British and the French.

_____

_____**10.** The Treaty of Paris gave Britain a claim to all French lands east of the Mississippi River.

_____

Name _____ Class _____ Date _____

FILL IN THE BLANK *10 points each* For each of the following statements, fill in the blank with the appropriate word, phrase, or name.

1. The first people to settle in the British colonies built communities and farms close to the _____ coastline or to major rivers.

2. Gradually, European settlers moved into the Virginia and Carolina _____ , the frontier region between the coastal settlements and the Appalachian Mountains.

3. In the 1760s, a rising number of settlers began crossing the Appalachian Mountains because the British victory in the _____ War had reduced the concern about Indian raids and renewed interest in settling in the western lands.

4. After the signing of the Treaty of Paris, Britain replaced _____ as the European power in the Ohio River valley.

5. The British assumed that the North American territory it had won in the French and Indian War included all _____ lands as well.

6. Chief _____ emerged as the leader of a group of Indian tribes determined to force the British from their land.

7. An unsuccessful, months-long attack on Fort _____ resulted in the Indian warriors returning to their villages.

8. The _____ banned any further British colonial settlement west of the Appalachian Mountains, creating a dividing line between colonial and Indian lands.

9. Although the new law had strong support in the British government, many of the colonists _____ it.

10. The new law was difficult to enforce and was ignored by most people who wanted to settle or trade in the _____ valley.

Name _____ Class _____ Date _____

MATCHING *10 points each* Match each of the following people or terms with the correct description by writing the letter of the description in the space provided. Some descriptions will not be used.

_____**1.** George Grenville

_____**2.** Sugar Act

_____**3.** Currency Act

_____**4.** Vice-Admiralty

_____**5.** Committees of Correspondence

_____**6.** boycott

_____**7.** Stamp Act

_____**8.** Sons of Liberty

_____**9.** Patrick Henry

_____**10.** William Pitt

a. Boston lawyer who wrote an essay attacking Parliament's unfair taxation of the American colonists

b. member of Parliament who believed that the Stamp Act was unjust and who persuaded Parliament to repeal it

c. first law passed by Parliament specifically designed to raise money in the American colonies

d. popular method of protest among the colonies in which the colonists would refuse to buy certain British goods

e. Virginian who presented a series of resolutions to the House of Burgesses stating that the Stamp Act violated the rights of the colonists as British citizens

f. secret colonial societies that used violence to frighten tax collectors

g. British prime minister who looked to the American colonists to pay Great Britain's debts from the French and Indian War

h. abolish an act or law

i. types of courts in which suspected smugglers were assumed to be guilty until they were proven innocent

j. groups of colonists that contacted towns and colonies to share ideas and information about new British laws and ways to challenge them

k. law passed by Parliament requiring colonists to pay for an official stamp whenever they bought paper items such as newspapers, pamphlets, licenses, and playing cards

l. law passed by Parliament that banned the colonies from printing their own money

CHAPTER

6

Conflicts in the Colonies

★ ★

DAILY QUIZ 6.4

MULTIPLE CHOICE *10 points each* For each of the following, write the letter of the *best* choice in the space provided.

_____ **1.** Many colonists thought that the Townshend Acts
   a. should be replaced by a Stamp Act.
   b. had the best interest of the colonies at heart.
   c. took too much power away from the colonies and gave it to royal officials.
   d. would be a good way to help Parliament raise money.

_____ **2.** Colonial women played a key role in the boycott of British goods by
   a. buying all the British cloth and other goods they could afford.
   b. throwing British cloth and food into Boston Harbor.
   c. buying French food and cloth instead.
   d. making cloth and other necessary goods at home.

_____ **3.** The Boston Massacre occurred as a result of
   a. passage of the Intolerable Acts by colonial legislatures.
   b. enforcement of the Townshend Acts by British soldiers.
   c. passage of the Tea Act by Parliament.
   d. the Boston Tea Party.

_____ **4.** Whose ship was seized by tax collectors on suspicion of smuggling?
   a. Crispus Attucks
   b. John Hancock
   c. Samuel Adams
   d. Thomas Gage

_____ **5.** The colonists who participated in the Boston Tea Party
   a. disguised themselves as Indians.
   b. were caught and sent to prison.
   c. apologized to the British government.
   d. disguised themselves as British officers.

_____ **6.** The Tea Act of 1773
   a. gave colonial merchants the right to sell their tea directly to Britain.
   b. banned the sale of tea in the colonies.
   c. gave the British East India Company permission to sell its tea directly to the colonies.
   d. banned all tax on tea in the colonies.

_____ **7.** As a result of the Boston Tea Party,
   a. Massachusetts was given a charter.
   b. the colonial legislatures passed the Intolerable Acts.
   c. Parliament passed the Coercive Acts.
   d. Britain repealed the Quartering Act.

_____ **8.** Who was Mercy Otis Warren?
   a. the leader of the Sons of Liberty
   b. the governor of Massachusetts
   c. the first person killed in the Boston Massacre
   d. a writer who criticized the actions of the British government

_____ **9.** The writs of assistance
   a. allowed colonial women to buy British cloth at reduced prices.
   b. allowed tax collectors to search for smuggled goods.
   c. helped colonists pay for imported tea.
   d. helped each colony prepare its own charter and form its own legislature.

_____ **10.** Following the Boston Massacre, Britain's Parliament
   a. repealed the Townshend Acts but kept the tax on tea.
   b. repealed the tax on tea but passed a new tax on coffee.
   c. repealed the Stamp Act but kept the tax on sugar.
   d. repealed the tax on tea and repealed the Intolerable Acts.

Name _____ Class _____ Date _____

★ ★

GEOGRAPHY AND HISTORY QUIZ

A Shift in Power

FILL IN THE BLANK *10 points each*   For each of the following statements, fill in the blank with the appropriate word, phrase, or name.

1. As more Europeans settled in North America, _____ found themselves being pushed farther and farther west.

2. Because of conflicts with Chief Metacomet of the Wampanoag and other Indian groups, colonial growth in New England _____ for several decades in the late 1600s.

3. As a result of King Philip's War, a bitter conflict between New England colonists and the Wampanoag, American Indians were forced to accept both colonial _____ and the loss of more land.

4. During the 1700s, increasing numbers of _____ brought to the colonies made up a significant part of the total colonial population.

5. _____ , the colony with the largest population, grew rapidly after the 1730s as settlers spread west beyond the colony's tidewater area seeking less expensive land suitable for farming.

6. One reason that the population in the colonies grew at a faster rate than in Britain was that more women _____ in the colonies than in Britain, often at a younger age, and had more children.

7. Of the British, French, and Spanish colonies that existed in eastern North America in 1760, the _____ colonies had the largest population and the _____ colonies had the smallest population.

8. In the mid-1750s, Britain and _____ were in dispute over land to the south of the original thirteen British colonies.

9. By 1763 the British in North America had taken control of _____ away from the French.

10. France surrendered _____ to Spain in 1762, but Spain never really exercised control over this huge territory located west of the Mississippi River.

★ ★

DAILY QUIZ 7.1

MULTIPLE CHOICE *10 points each* For each of the following, write the letter of the *best* choice in the space provided.

_____ **1.** The British sent troops to Concord to
   a. fight the American army there.
   b. capture General George Washington.
   c. seize the local militia's weapons that were stored there.
   d. hold the town under siege.

_____ **2.** The main purpose of the First Continental Congress was to
   a. decide how to declare war on Britain.
   b. decide what to do about the continuing British abuses of the colonists.
   c. inform the British that they must leave American territory.
   d. decide how to pay for war supplies.

_____ **3.** Why was the fighting at Lexington significant?
   a. It forced the British to retreat.
   b. It saved the town from the British.
   c. It marked the end of British rule in the colonies.
   d. It was the first battle of the American Revolution.

_____ **4.** The members of the colonial militias were known as
   a. Olive Branches.
   b. Minutemen.
   c. Greencoats.
   d. Redcoats.

_____ **5.** The attack on Fort Ticonderoga was important because it
   a. resulted in the capture of valuable British weapons.
   b. destroyed the fort.
   c. stopped the British advance.
   d. made Benedict Arnold a national hero.

_____ **6.** Who led the attack on Fort Ticonderoga?
   a. Thomas Gage and William Howe
   b. George Washington
   c. Ethan Allen and Benedict Arnold
   d. John Adams and Samuel Adams

_____ **7.** The Second Continental Congress did all of the following *EXCEPT*
   a. plan a Continental Army.
   b. appoint George Washington as commander of the Continental Army.
   c. send the Olive Branch Petition to King George III.
   d. meet with King George III to discuss peace terms.

_____ **8.** After the British retreated to Boston, the colonists
   a. burned the town of Concord.
   b. forced the British in Boston to surrender.
   c. imposed a naval blockade on Boston.
   d. placed Boston under siege.

_____ **9.** The geography of the Boston area helped the colonists because
   a. the hills around the city provided a good position from which to attack.
   b. the land was very flat, allowing easy access to the city.
   c. the city was on the seashore.
   d. the climate made life difficult for the British.

_____ **10.** Once the colonists brought their cannons to Dorchester Heights, the British
   a. accepted the Olive Branch Petition.
   b. retreated to Canada.
   c. surrendered.
   d. marched south.

TRUE/FALSE *10 points each*   Indicate whether each statement below is true or false by writing *T* or *F* in the space provided. If the statement is false, explain why.

_____**1.** In *Common Sense,* Thomas Paine argued that the colonists should immediately halt the revolt against Great Britain.

_____

_____**2.** Thomas Paine wrote as a common man to common people.

_____

_____**3.** The main argument of *Common Sense* was that people should be ruled by monarchies.

_____

_____**4.** The primary author of the Declaration of Independence was Thomas Jefferson.

_____

_____**5.** The writers of the Declaration largely drew inspiration from Thomas Hobbes, who argued that people need monarchs because they are unable to govern themselves.

_____

_____**6.** The Declaration of Independence made each colony an independent nation.

_____

_____**7.** The Declaration of Independence did not specifically mention women or slaves.

_____

_____**8.** Abigail Adams wanted the signers of the Declaration to protect the rights of women.

_____

_____**9.** Patriots supported the British, while Loyalists supported independence.

_____

_____**10.** In 1781 a Massachusetts slave named Mum Bett successfully sued for her freedom based on the principles of the Declaration of Independence.

_____

Name _____ Class _____ Date _____

MATCHING *10 points each* Match each of the following people or terms with the correct description by writing the letter of the description in the space provided. Some descriptions will not be used.

_____ **1.** Thayendanegea   _____ **6.** Peter Salem

_____ **2.** Mary Ludwig Hays   _____ **7.** Deborah Sampson

_____ **3.** James Forten   _____ **8.** Richard Montgomery

_____ **4.** Joseph Brant   _____ **9.** Benedict Arnold

_____ **5.** Lord Dunmore's Proclamation   _____ **10.** William Howe

a. general who served as head of the Continental Army

b. order issued by the royal governor of Virginia offering freedom to any slave who would fight for the British

c. Patriot general who led the attack on St. Johns, Canada, and whose troops captured Montreal

d. Patriot who earned the nickname "Molly Pitcher" by bringing water to Patriot troops

e. member of a local militia who, like all African Americans, was initially prohibited from serving in the Continental Army by order of General Washington

f. British general who forced the Continental Army to abandon Long Island

g. Mohawk leader who fought for the British during the Revolution

h. Patriot general who led his troops north through what is now Maine to launch an attack on Quebec

i. Patriot who disguised herself as a man in order to fight

j. Patriot teenager who fetched gunpowder for sailors in the Continental Navy

k. Indian ally of the British who was also known as Thayendanegea

l. hired foreign soldiers who fight in a war

Name _____ Class _____ Date _____

The American Revolution

★ ★ ★ ★ ★ ★ ★ ★ ★ ★ ★ ★ ★ ★ ★ ★ ★ ★ ★ ★

DAILY QUIZ 7.4

FILL IN THE BLANK *10 points each*   For each of the following statements, fill in the blank with the appropriate word, phrase, or name.

1. After the Patriot victory at the Battle of _____ , the French formally declared their support for the Patriot cause.

2. One of the greatest American naval heroes of the Revolution was _____ , who defeated the British warship *Serapis* with his ship, the *Bonhomme Richard*.

3. On December 26, 1776, General Washington and his troops soundly defeated the Hessian forces at the Battle of _____ .

4. The primary Patriot naval strategy was to stop the flow of British _____ coming from the West Indies to North America.

5. General George Washington attacked and defeated the British forces at the Battle of _____ only a few days after his victory at Trenton.

6. In the summer of 1777 the _____ , a 20-year-old Frenchman who spoke little English, arrived in the United States to help the colonists battle the British.

7. When George Washington met the British forces at the Battle of _____ near Philadelphia, the Patriots suffered heavy losses and were forced to retreat.

8. Like the French, the Spanish had been secretly aiding the Patriot cause, and _____ , the governor of Spanish Louisiana, was particularly helpful.

9. Thaddeus _____ came from Poland to lend his engineering skills to the Patriot cause.

10. General John _____ led the British troops against the Americans at the Battle of Saratoga.

Name _____ Class _____ Date _____

The American Revolution

★ ★

DAILY QUIZ 7.5

MULTIPLE CHOICE *10 points each* For each of the following, write the letter of the *best* choice in the space provided.

_____ **1.** The British forces were prevented from escaping at Yorktown because
  a. British troops had become sick from malnutrition.
  b. they had no horses or wagons.
  c. all of their military leaders had been killed.
  d. a French fleet kept British ships from providing aid.

_____ **2.** The greatest Patriot victory in the West was at the Battle of
  a. Vincennes.
  b. Camden.
  c. Charleston.
  d. Yorktown.

_____ **3.** After their defeat at Saratoga, the British decided to
  a. end the war.
  b. concentrate their efforts on the southern colonies.
  c. concentrate their efforts on capturing New England.
  d. retreat to Canada.

_____ **4.** One of the worst defeats for the Patriots came at the Battle of
  a. Camden.
  b. Saratoga.
  c. Yorktown.
  d. Vincennes.

_____ **5.** After their loss at Camden, the Patriots in the South resorted mainly to
  a. a policy of retreat.
  b. considering surrender.
  c. guerrilla warfare.
  d. using the same military tactics as the British.

_____ **6.** The American Revolution formally came to an end with
  a. the defeat at Camden.
  b. the Treaty of Paris of 1783.
  c. the capture of Vincennes.
  d. the French involvement in the war.

_____ **7.** George Rogers Clark hoped to weaken the British support system in the West by first capturing the villages of
  a. Detroit and St. Louis.
  b. Charleston and Savannah.
  c. Kaskaskia and Cahokia.
  d. Camden and Yorktown.

_____ **8.** The Battle of Yorktown was significant because
  a. it led the British to ask for peace.
  b. it marked the beginning of a new Patriot campaign in the South.
  c. it wiped out the Continental Army.
  d. it gave the British forces new hope of success.

_____ **9.** One of the greatest guerrilla warriors of the Revolution was
  a. George Washington.
  b. Francis Marion.
  c. Benedict Arnold.
  d. Horatio Gates.

_____ **10.** In the Treaty of Paris of 1783, the United States gained
  a. official recognition of its independence from Britain.
  b. recognition of its national borders.
  c. acceptance of the rights of its citizens to settle and trade west of the original thirteen colonies.
  d. all of the above.

Name _____ Class _____ Date _____

DAILY QUIZ 8.1

MATCHING *10 points each* Match each of the following people or terms with the correct description by writing the letter of the description in the space provided. Some descriptions will not be used.

_____**1.** John Locke

_____**2.** republic

_____**3.** Virginia Statute for Religious Freedom

_____**4.** Articles of Confederation

_____**5.** Confederation Congress

_____**6.** ratification

_____**7.** Land Ordinance of 1785

_____**8.** Northwest Territory

_____**9.** Baron de Montesquieu

_____**10.** constitution

a. formal approval that had to be given by all 13 state legislatures before the Articles of Confederation could go into effect

b. political philosopher who believed that a social contract existed between political leaders and the people they governed, and that part of this contract included the government's duty to protect the people's natural rights

c. vast region that included present-day Illinois, Indiana, Michigan, Ohio, and Wisconsin

d. another term for voting rights

e. legislation that protected religious freedom and forbade the establishment of an official church

f. act passed by Congress that created a system of limited self-government for the settlers living in the Northwest Territory

g. governing body for the states under the Articles of Confederation, in which each state had one vote

h. French philosopher who argued that the only way people could achieve liberty was through the separation of governmental powers

i. type of government in which the head of state is elected and in which the people hold the political power

j. set of basic principles and laws that determine the powers and duties of the government

k. surveys that divided public lands into townships of 36 square miles, which in turn were divided into 36 lots of 640 acres each

l. document that created "a firm league of friendship" among the states

CHAPTER

8

Forming a Government

★ ★

DAILY QUIZ 8.2

FILL IN THE BLANK *10 points each* For each of the following statements, fill in the blank with the appropriate word, phrase, or name.

1. Under the _____ , Congress could not force states to provide soldiers for an army, which made it difficult to enforce international treaties.

2. After the Treaty of Paris was signed, the British banned U.S. ships from bringing trade goods to Canada and forced American merchants to pay high _____ in order to sell certain goods in Britain.

3. Taking advantage of the weakness of the United States, Spanish officials in 1784 closed the lower _____ to U.S. shipping.

4. Although American merchants pursued new trade markets in China, France, and the Netherlands, _____ remained the United States's most important trading partner.

5. In addition to international trade problems, trade among the states became a problem because the Confederation Congress had no power to regulate _____ .

6. Inflation also became a problem in the United States because each state had the power to issue its own _____ .

7. In many states, inflation helped _____ because they were able to pay off debts with currency that had lost value since they had borrowed it.

8. Massachusetts's refusal to issue paper money, its attempt to pay off war debts by levying taxes on land, and trade restrictions combined to create a(n) _____ , a steep drop in economic activity.

9. _____ was a revolt by farmers who were hard hit by Massachusetts's economic policy and could not pay their debts.

10. After the revolt of the farmers in Massachusetts, many people began calling for a stronger _____ government that would be able to protect the nation in times of crisis.

MULTIPLE CHOICE *10 points each* For each of the following, write the letter of the *best* choice in the space provided.

_____ **1.** The Constitutional Convention was held in
  a. New York City.
  b. Washington, D.C.
  c. Philadelphia.
  d. Williamsburg.

_____ **2.** Who was elected president of the Constitutional Convention?
  a. Benjamin Franklin
  b. Thomas Jefferson
  c. James Madison
  d. George Washington

_____ **3.** No women, African Americans, or American Indians participated in the Constitutional Convention because members of these groups
  a. were happy with the Articles.
  b. were invited to the convention but refused to come.
  c. were not yet granted the rights of full citizens.
  d. had already ratified the Articles.

_____ **4.** Which of the following statements about the Great Compromise is *NOT* correct?
  a. Each state would be represented equally with one vote in a one-house legislature.
  b. In the lower house, each state would receive one representative for every 40,000 inhabitants.
  c. Every state, regardless of size, would have an equal vote in the upper legislative house.
  d. It combined elements of the New Jersey Plan and the Virginia Plan.

_____ **5.** The judicial branch of government
  a. administers the laws.
  b. makes the laws.
  c. enforces the laws.
  d. interprets the laws.

_____ **6.** What did the delegates decide on the issue of the slave trade?
  a. The slave trade could continue without interference for 20 years.
  b. The slave trade would be banned.
  c. Each state could decide whether or not to participate in the slave trade.
  d. The slave trade could continue without interference indefinitely.

_____ **7.** The purpose of the Constitutional Convention was to
  a. discuss revising the Articles of Confederation.
  b. make each state a free and independent nation.
  c. help each state write a constitution.
  d. ratify the Articles of Confederation.

_____ **8.** The new government would be based on federalism, which
  a. allows each state to create its own federal government.
  b. gives all power to a strong central government.
  c. distributes power between a central authority and the states.
  d. makes state law the law of the land.

_____ **9.** The executive branch of government
  a. makes the laws.
  b. includes the president and the administrative departments.
  c. is made up of all the national courts.
  d. is made up of the Senate and the House of Representatives.

_____ **10.** To prevent any branch of government from becoming too powerful, the framers of the Constitution created
  a. the New Jersey Plan.
  b. a system of checks and balances.
  c. the Three-Fifths Compromise.
  d. a two-house legislature.

TRUE/FALSE *10 points each* Indicate whether each statement below is true or false by writing *T* or *F* in the space provided. If the statement is false, explain why.

_____ **1.** Benjamin Franklin urged the delegates to reject the new Constitution.

_____

_____ **2.** Two of the three delegates who refused to sign the Constitution thought that it needed a bill of rights.

_____

_____ **3.** People who opposed the Constitution were known as Anticonstitutionalists.

_____

_____ **4.** People who supported the Constitution believed it provided a good balance of power and reflected a carefully considered compromise among a variety of political opinions.

_____

_____ **5.** The *Federalist Papers* were written by George Washington and Thomas Jefferson.

_____

_____ **6.** The Constitution required the ratification of all 13 states before it could go into effect.

_____

_____ **7.** Each state except Rhode Island held special state conventions to give ordinary citizens the opportunity to discuss and vote on whether the Constitution should be ratified.

_____

_____ **8.** Delaware was the first state to ratify the Constitution.

_____

_____ **9.** In July of 1788 Congress declared the new Constitution ratified.

_____

_____ **10.** The first five amendments to the Constitution make up the Bill of Rights.

_____

★ ★

GEOGRAPHY AND HISTORY QUIZ

The Living Constitution

MULTIPLE CHOICE *10 points each* For each of the following, write the letter of the *best* choice in the space provided.

_____ **1.** The original 13 states contained fewer than
   a. 4,000 people.
   b. 40,000 people.
   c. 400,000 people.
   d. 4 million people.

_____ **2.** How many people had to be living in a territory before the territory was eligible to become a state?
   a. 5,000
   b. 20,000
   c. 60,000
   d. 100,000

_____ **3.** For a territory to become a state, the territory's proposed constitution had to be approved by
   a. the Supreme Court.
   b. the president of the United States.
   c. Congress.
   d. the Senate.

_____ **4.** Which of the following constitutional amendments lowered the minimum voting age from 21 to 18?
   a. Fifteenth Amendment
   b. Nineteenth Amendment
   c. Twenty-second Amendment
   d. Twenty-sixth Amendment

_____ **5.** What proportion of Senate seats are up for election during each midterm election?
   a. one quarter
   b. one third
   c. one half
   d. all

_____ **6.** Which constitutional amendment limits U.S. presidents to two terms in office?
   a. Twenty-second Amendment
   b. Nineteenth Amendment
   c. Sixteenth Amendment
   d. Twenty-seventh Amendment

_____ **7.** Supreme Court justices
   a. serve for life.
   b. are appointed by the Senate and approved by the president.
   c. must live in the state where elected.
   d. must be at least 25 years old.

_____ **8.** How many congressional districts are there in the United States today?
   a. 106
   b. 265
   c. 380
   d. 435

_____ **9.** The first three states to ratify the U.S. Constitution were
   a. Delaware, Pennsylvania, and New Jersey.
   b. New Hampshire, West Virginia, and Tennessee.
   c. Maryland, Florida, and Connecticut.
   d. South Carolina, North Carolina, and Virginia.

_____ **10.** To be eligible to become a senator, a U.S. citizen must be
   a. 25 years old.
   b. 30 years old.
   c. 35 years old.
   d. 40 years old.

MATCHING *10 points each* Match each of the following terms with its correct description by writing the letter of the correct description in the space provided. Some descriptions will not be used.

_____ **1.** delegated powers

_____ **2.** elastic clause

_____ **3.** reserved powers

_____ **4.** concurrent powers

_____ **5.** representative democracy

_____ **6.** House of Representatives

_____ **7.** Speaker of the House

_____ **8.** president pro tempore

_____ **9.** impeach

_____ **10.** executive orders

a. larger of the two houses of Congress, with a current membership of 435

b. powers granted to the federal government, including the power to coin money, to regulate interstate and international trade, and to declare war

c. bring charges against a president who may have committed a crime or violated the essential presidential duties

d. those powers retained by the state governments or by citizens, such as conducting elections, establishing local governments, and regulating education

e. smaller of the two houses of Congress, with a current membership of 100

f. those powers shared by both the federal and state governments, including the power to tax, to borrow money, and to enforce laws

g. leader of the Senate in the absence of the vice president

h. Article I, Section 8, of the Constitution, which allows Congress to stretch its delegated powers to address issues that the nation's founders could not have foreseen

i. issued by the president to carry out laws that affect administrative matters or executive policy

j. government by representatives of the people

k. member of the majority party who leads the House of Representatives

l. cancel legislation

Citizenship and the Constitution

★ ★

DAILY QUIZ 9.2

TRUE/FALSE *10 points each*   Indicate whether each statement below is true or false by writing *T* or *F* in the space provided. If the statement is false, explain why.

_____**1.** James Madison is often called the Father of the Constitution.

_____

_____**2.** The First Amendment permits the government to support an official religion.

_____

_____**3.** The freedom of speech does not mean that people can say anything they want to say.

_____

_____**4.** The right of petition enables Americans to express their dissatisfaction with current laws or to suggest new ones.

_____

_____**5.** Because the Fourth Amendment protects against unreasonable searches and seizures, officials must obtain a search warrant before they can search a person's home.

_____

_____**6.** The goal of the Fifth, Sixth, Seventh, and Eighth Amendments is to ensure that the rights of crime victims are fully protected.

_____

_____**7.** Anyone found not guilty in a criminal trial cannot be tried again for the same crime.

_____

_____**8.** Government has the right to take personal property when it is in the public's interest.

_____

_____**9.** The Seventh Amendment gives people accused of crimes the right to have an attorney.

_____

_____**10.** The Eighth Amendment bans government from giving cruel and unusual punishments.

_____

Name _____ Class _____ Date _____

Citizenship and the Constitution

★ ★

DAILY QUIZ 9.3

FILL IN THE BLANK *10 points each*   For each of the following statements, fill in the blank with the appropriate word, phrase, or name.

1. People born in a foreign country whose parents are not U.S. citizens can become citizens only if they move to the United States and go through a process called _____ .

2. The U.S. government has the right to _____ , or return to his or her country of origin, any immigrant who breaks the law or who is in the country illegally.

3. The only distinctions between naturalized and native-born citizens are that naturalized citizens can lose their citizenship and they cannot become _____ or _____ of the United States.

4. All citizens have a responsibility to stay informed about the issues and to be aware of changes in _____ that affect them.

5. The government relies on _____ to pay for the many services it provides to citizens.

6. Most funding for public schools comes from _____ .

7. All citizens face the possibility of being called for _____ , which involves listening to a court case and reaching a verdict on it.

8. In order to make rational decisions, voters must be wary of _____ , or material that is slanted deliberately to support or harm a cause.

9. Citizens who wish to can make financial contributions to political candidates directly or through _____ .

10. Some groups in the United States, called _____ groups, lobby for issues that affect all Americans.

DAILY QUIZ 10.1

FILL IN THE BLANK *10 points each* For each of the following statements, fill in the blank with the appropriate word, phrase, or name.

1. On April 6, 1789, _____ was unanimously selected as president of the United States by the electoral college.

2. Republican _____ , the idea that women played an important role in teaching their children to be good citizens, became more widespread in the young nation.

3. At the time the new nation was launched, only two U.S. cities, _____ and _____ , had populations greater than 25,000.

4. The first capital of the United States was in _____ , whose population had grown to 33,000 by 1790.

5. After Congress created several executive departments, each specializing in a different area of national policy, the president chose _____ as the first secretary of state.

6. Together, the heads of the executive departments became known as the president's _____ and as a group served to advise the president.

7. The judicial branch of government also was in need of organization, because the _____ did not specify how many federal courts there should be, where they should be located, or how many federal judges would be needed.

8. The _____ , passed by Congress in September 1789, created a federal court system with three levels.

9. The _____ , which had six justices, occupied the top level of the federal court system.

10. The president appointed _____ to serve as the first chief justice of the United States.

Name _____ Class _____ Date _____

TRUE/FALSE *10 points each*   Indicate whether each statement below is true or false by writing *T* or *F* in the space provided. If the statement is false, explain why.

_____ **1.** Alexander Hamilton's biggest challenge was finding a way to pay off the national debt.

_____

_____ **2.** Because investors were worried that the government would not be able to pay off its debt, many bondholders decided to sell their bonds at a fraction of their original value.

_____

_____ **3.** Hamilton and Jefferson agreed that it was fair for speculators to make a profit.

_____

_____ **4.** In a compromise move, a new national capital was chosen and the federal government assumed the debts owed by the states for Revolutionary War expenses.

_____

_____ **5.** Thomas Jefferson believed in a strong central government.

_____

_____ **6.** Although Hamilton pushed for an economy based on manufacturing and commerce, Jefferson thought that the nation would be better served by remaining agricultural.

_____

_____ **7.** Hamilton proposed the creation of a national mint to issue money and a national bank.

_____

_____ **8.** Jefferson believed in a loose construction of the Constitution.

_____

_____ **9.** The president and Congress supported Hamilton's plan for a national bank.

_____

_____ **10.** The national bank proved to be disastrous for the economy and was quickly closed.

_____

MULTIPLE CHOICE *10 points each* For each of the following, write the letter of the *best* choice in the space provided.

_____ **1.** One of the first acts of the French Revolution was
 a. the assassination of the French king.
 b. the storming of the Bastille.
 c. the burning of the royal palace.
 d. the invasion of France by Russians.

_____ **2.** Who was serving as the U.S. ambassador to France at the time of the French Revolution?
 a. Alexander Hamilton
 b. George Washington
 c. James Madison
 d. Thomas Jefferson

_____ **3.** The U.S. response to the war between France and Britain was to
 a. declare war on France.
 b. declare war on both Britain and France.
 c. remain neutral toward all nations at war in Europe.
 d. declare war on Britain.

_____ **4.** When Edmond Genet arrived in the United States, he
 a. immediately went to speak to President Washington.
 b. pleaded with Congress to declare war on France.
 c. began recruiting privateers.
 d. brought French troops to attack the U.S. capital.

_____ **5.** Why did Thomas Jefferson resign as the U.S. secretary of state?
 a. He was upset by the U.S. policy toward France and Hamilton's interference in foreign policy.
 b. Washington was unhappy with his work and asked him to resign.
 c. Ill health forced him to resign.
 d. He accepted a top position in the French government.

_____ **6.** Jay's Treaty was signed in order to
 a. end the fighting between France and Britain.
 b. prevent another war between Britain and the United States.
 c. end the French Revolution.
 d. end the hostilities between Jefferson and Hamilton.

_____ **7.** Because of problems between Americans and the Spanish,
 a. Spain gave Florida to the British.
 b. Spain declared war on the United States.
 c. the U.S. Army forced the Spanish to leave Florida.
 d. Spain closed the port of New Orleans to all U.S. trade.

_____ **8.** Pinckney's Treaty was most favorable
 a. to Spain.
 b. to France.
 c. to the United States.
 d. to Britain.

_____ **9.** Americans who were opposed to the French Revolution
 a. worried about the increasing attacks on all forms of authority.
 b. had also opposed the American Revolution.
 c. demanded that Congress pass an amendment to end it.
 d. felt that only Americans should try to change their government.

_____ **10.** Washington wanted right of deposit at the port of New Orleans because it
 a. would let Americans live in Florida.
 b. would let American boats transfer their goods at New Orleans without paying cargo fees.
 c. would give access to the fur trade.
 d. was the only route to the West.

FILL IN THE BLANK *10 points each* For each of the following statements, fill in the blank with the appropriate word, phrase, or name.

1. In 1790 Miami chief _____ and a force from the Indian confederation defeated U.S. forces in the Northwest Territory.

2. After "Mad Anthony" Wayne and his troops defeated the Indian confederation at the Battle of _____ , Wayne's forces burned the Indians' villages and fields.

3. In August 1795, leaders of the Indian confederation signed the _____ , which gave the United States access to some Indian lands in the Northwest Territory and guaranteed safe travel for U.S. citizens crossing Indian lands in that region.

4. During the _____ , which began as a protest by farmers forced to pay a tax on the alcohol they made for trade, tax collectors were tarred and feathered.

5. George Washington and _____ led an army of more than 10,000 soldiers to Pennsylvania to put down the rebellious farmers.

6. In 1796 George Washington decided not to run for a _____ term as president of the United States.

7. By stepping down from office Washington sought to remind Americans that he was their president, not their king, and that the _____ were the true leaders of the United States.

8. In his _____ , Washington spoke about what he believed to be the three greatest threats to the nation: public debt, dangerous foreign alliances, and political divisions at home.

9. Washington recommended that the government seldom _____ and avoid the "accumulation of debt."

10. Washington's experience with disagreements between political groups in the United States had convinced him that political _____ was important for national success.

MATCHING *10 points each* Match each of the following people or terms with the correct description by writing the letter of the description in the space provided. Some descriptions will not be used.

_____**1.** political parties

_____**2.** Federalist Party

_____**3.** Democratic-Republican Party

_____**4.** John Adams

_____**5.** Thomas Jefferson

_____**6.** XYZ affair

_____**7.** Alien and Sedition Acts

_____**8.** Virginia and Kentucky Resolutions

_____**9.** House of Representatives

_____**10.** Twelfth Amendment

a. arguments stating that the Alien and Sedition Acts were unconstitutional because they went beyond the powers granted to the federal government and interfered with the powers of the state governments

b. situation in which French agents told a U.S. diplomatic team that French minister Talleyrand would discuss a treaty only in exchange for a $250,000 bribe and a loan of $12 million from the United States

c. political party that wanted to strengthen the power of the federal government and to promote industry and trade

d. person who ran with Thomas Jefferson against John Adams and Charles Pinckney in the 1800 presidential election

e. one of the three U.S. diplomats involved in the XYZ affair

f. political party that wanted to preserve the power of the state governments

g. person who served as vice president under John Adams

h. groups that organize to help elect government officials and to influence government policies

i. laws that allowed the president to expel foreign citizens suspected of treason and made it illegal to use false or hostile words against the government or its policies

j. person who won the 1796 presidential election and became the second president of the United States

k. constitutional amendment ratified in 1804 that created a separate ballot for president and vice president

l. governmental body that broke the tie between Thomas Jefferson and Aaron Burr in the 1800 presidential election

TRUE/FALSE *10 points each*   Indicate whether each statement below is true or false by writing *T* or *F* in the space provided. If the statement is false, explain why.

_____**1.** Along with Thomas Jefferson's victory in the 1800 election, the Federalist Party had won control of both houses of Congress from the Republican Party.

_____

_____**2.** The victory of Thomas Jefferson and the Republicans gave proof that the leadership of the United States could change hands peacefully.

_____

_____**3.** Jefferson was the first president to be inaugurated in the capital city of Washington.

_____

_____**4.** Once in office, Jefferson increased military spending and increased domestic taxes.

_____

_____**5.** Although Jefferson had battled Alexander Hamilton over the constitutionality of the Bank of the United States, as president he kept the Bank in place.

_____

_____**6.** Under pressure from both Republicans and Federalists, Jefferson agreed to replace a number of Federalist officials with Republicans, but refused to replace all Federalists.

_____

_____**7.** Jefferson was concerned about the number of Federalist judges appointed by Adams.

_____

_____**8.** Chief Justice John Marshall and President Jefferson agreed on all political issues.

_____

_____**9.** The case of *Marbury* v. *Madison* established the principle of judicial review.

_____

_____**10.** The principle of judicial review caused the Supreme Court to lose a great deal of power.

_____

MULTIPLE CHOICE *10 points each* For each of the following, write the letter of the *best* choice in the space provided.

_____ **1.** In 1800 Napoleon Bonaparte controlled
   a. Great Britain.
   b. Spain.
   c. Germany.
   d. France.

_____ **2.** Who was Toussaint L'Ouverture?
   a. a former slave who became leader of Saint Domingue after a slave revolt
   b. the king of France
   c. the U.S. ambassador to France
   d. the Spanish official who secretly traded Louisiana to France

_____ **3.** U.S. leaders were concerned about French ownership of Louisiana because
   a. they thought that the British had the right to own and occupy Louisiana.
   b. they had already made an agreement to buy Louisiana from the Spanish.
   c. they feared that the French would persuade Louisiana Indian tribes to attack the Americans.
   d. it could block future U.S. expansion westward and interfere with trade along the Mississippi River.

_____ **4.** The United States bought Louisiana from France in 1803 at a cost of
   a. $1 million.
   b. $15 million.
   c. $100 million.
   d. $150 million.

_____ **5.** The Louisiana Purchase
   a. did not occur until Congress passed an amendment approving it.
   b. doubled the size of the United States.
   c. offered the United States an opportunity to expand its commercial and manufacturing industries.
   d. tripled the size of the United States.

_____ **6.** The members of the Lewis and Clark expedition were told to
   a. explore the Colorado River and remove all Indians from U.S. land.
   b. explore the Florida coastline and search for the Fountain of Youth.
   c. explore the Missouri River and establish peaceful relations with the American Indians they encountered.
   d. explore all lands east of the Mississippi River.

_____ **7.** Some of the most important help received by Lewis and Clark came from
   a. Sacagawea.
   b. Manuel de Godoy.
   c. Toussaint L'Ouverture.
   d. Robert Livingston.

_____ **8.** When Lewis and Clark met the Shoshoni, the Shoshoni
   a. gave them instructions on how to find the Atlantic Ocean.
   b. captured and imprisoned them.
   c. gave them horses and a guide to lead them across the Rocky Mountains.
   d. killed most of the members of the expedition.

_____ **9.** Some time after their expedition, Clark went on to become governor of the Missouri Territory and Lewis became
   a. governor of the Louisiana Territory.
   b. mayor of New Orleans.
   c. U.S. secretary of state.
   d. Speaker of the House.

_____ **10.** Zebulon Pike was sent to
   a. spy on British forts in the Southwest.
   b. find the Red River's starting point.
   c. locate the Mississippi River.
   d. sign a treaty with the Mandan.

Name _____ Class _____ Date _____

FILL IN THE BLANK *10 points each*   For each of the following statements, fill in the blank with the appropriate word, phrase, or name.

1. Like many of the European nations, the United States decided to pay a yearly tribute to the _____ States to keep them from capturing American ships.

2. Despite the protests of the U.S. government, the British _____ thousands of American citizens in their search for deserters.

3. Many Americans thought that the government should respond to British violations of U.S. neutrality with an _____ , or a ban on trade with Britain.

4. In 1809 Congress passed the _____ Act, which banned trade only with Britain and France and stated that the United States would renew trade with the first side that stopped violating U.S. neutrality.

5. The British government gave military aid to Indian nations in the _____ that were angry over the terms of the Treaty of Greenville and over the American settlement of lands beyond those covered in the treaty.

6. It was the dream of the Shawnee chief _____ to unite the Indians of the Northwest Territory, the South, and the eastern Mississippi Valley into a single confederation to oppose the American settlers.

7. The Battle of _____ occurred on November 7, 1811, after William Henry Harrison's forces marched close to the Indians and provoked an attack.

8. The _____ were members of Congress who thought that the best way to deal with Britain's actions was to declare war on Britain.

9. The strongest opponents of going to war with Britain were _____ from New England, who argued that they were more interested in renewing business ties with Britain than in fighting another war.

10. _____ served as president and commander in chief during the War of 1812.

The Expanding Nation

★ ★ ★ ★ ★ ★ ★ ★ ★ ★ ★ ★ ★ ★ ★ ★ ★ ★ ★ ★

DAILY QUIZ 11.4

MATCHING *10 points each*   Match each of the following people or terms with the correct description by writing the letter of the description in the space provided. Some descriptions will not be used.

_____ **1.** "Old Ironsides"

_____ **2.** Oliver Hazard Perry

_____ **3.** Battle of Lake Erie

_____ **4.** Battle of the Thames

_____ **5.** Andrew Jackson

_____ **6.** Chief Red Eagle

_____ **7.** Dolley Madison

_____ **8.** Battle of New Orleans

_____ **9.** Hartford Convention

_____ **10.** Treaty of Ghent

a. Indian leader whose warriors joined with the British to defeat one American army and capture Fort Detroit in present-day Michigan

b. American general whose victory in the Battle of Horseshoe Bend led to a treaty that forced the Creek to give up millions of acres of their land

c. nickname for the USS *Constitution*, which won one of the first battles of the War of 1812

d. Connecticut meeting of Federalists to protest the war, which resulted in the loss of much of the Federalists' political power

e. person who stayed to save valuables from the White House before the British burned it and other government buildings in Washington

f. battle that forced the British to withdraw and gave the U.S. Army new hope of victory in the war

g. British general who was persuaded by Tecumseh to make a stand by the Thames River against the Americans

h. agreement signed in Belgium on December 24, 1814, in which the war was ended and all conquered territory was restored

i. battle that resulted in more than 2,000 British casualties and nearly 100 U.S. casualties, fought two weeks after a peace treaty had been signed

j. Creek leader whose forces destroyed Fort Mims but who surrendered at the Battle of Horseshoe Bend

k. U.S. Navy captain whose job it was to break Britain's control of Lake Erie

l. battle in which Tecumseh was killed, weakening the Indian-British alliance around the Great Lakes

Name _____ Class _____ Date _____

★ ★

GEOGRAPHY AND HISTORY QUIZ

Expanding National Borders

TRUE/FALSE *20 points each* Indicate whether each statement below is true or false by writing *T* or *F* in the space provided. If the statement is false, explain why.

_____ **1.** In 1790 the United States was bordered on the south and the west by French-owned lands.

_____

_____ **2.** The land acquired by the United States in the Louisiana Purchase stretched all the way from the Mississippi River to the Rocky Mountains and nearly doubled the size of the country.

_____

_____ **3.** The average size of households in the United States was significantly larger than that of households in Britain because the United States had a higher birthrate and a higher standard of living.

_____

_____ **4.** The Adams-Onís Treaty of 1819 established the border between the United States and French territory.

_____

_____ **5.** Following its defeat by the Americans in the Revolutionary War, Britain refused to be a trading partner of the United States.

_____

Name _____ Class _____ Date _____

FILL IN THE BLANK *10 points each* For each of the following statements, fill in the blank with the appropriate word, phrase, or name.

1. After defeating the _____ in the War of 1812, the United States experienced a period of relative peace and national pride.

2. When James Monroe won the presidency in 1816, journalists wrote that the United States was entering the " _____ ."

3. In 1817 the United States and Britain signed the _____ , which limited naval power on the Great Lakes for both the United States and British Canada.

4. The _____ gave the United States fishing rights off parts of the Newfoundland and Labrador coasts and set the border between the United States and Canada at the 49th parallel, as far west as the Rocky Mountains.

5. When General Andrew Jackson crossed the border into Florida to capture Indian raiders, he started the First _____ War between U.S. and Indian forces.

6. With the signing of the Adams-Onís Treaty of 1819, _____ ceded Florida to the United States.

7. In exchange for receiving Florida under the Adams-Onís Treaty, the United States agreed to give up its claims to present-day _____ .

8. Simón Bolívar, nicknamed "The _____ ," led many of the fights for independence in Central and South America in the early 1800s.

9. After _____ broke free from Spain in 1821, President James Monroe became concerned that rival European powers might try to take control of the newly independent Latin American countries.

10. The _____ warned the European powers that North and South America were off limits to future colonization by any foreign power.

TRUE/FALSE *10 points each* Indicate whether each statement below is true or false by writing *T* or *F* in the space provided. If the statement is false, explain why.

_____ **1.** Missouri's application for statehood sparked great debate in Congress.

_____

_____ **2.** The Missouri Compromise, proposed by Henry Clay, would allow Missouri to enter the Union as a free state while Maine joined as a slave state.

_____

_____ **3.** Passage of the Missouri Compromise forever ended the U.S. debate over slavery.

_____

_____ **4.** The plan for using high tariffs to pay for internal improvements in the United States came to be known as the Improvement System.

_____

_____ **5.** It was difficult to travel by land in the early 1800s because most roads were dirt roads.

_____

_____ **6.** The first U.S. turnpike was a 66-mile toll road between Philadelphia and Lancaster.

_____

_____ **7.** The nation's first federal road project was the Washington Road.

_____

_____ **8.** The Erie Canal project ran from Albany to Buffalo, New York.

_____

_____ **9.** The five candidates in the 1824 presidential election all ran as Democrats.

_____

_____**10.** Andrew Jackson received the most popular votes in the 1824 presidential election but did not have the required number of electoral votes.

_____

DAILY QUIZ 12.3

MATCHING *10 points each*   Match each of the following people or terms with the correct description by writing the letter of the description in the space provided. Some descriptions will not be used.

_____**1.** nominating conventions   _____**6.** John C. Calhoun

_____ **2.** Democratic Party   _____**7.** John Marshall

_____ **3.** spoils system   _____**8.** Whig Party

_____ **4.** kitchen cabinet   _____**9.** Martin Van Buren

_____ **5.** Tariff of Abominations   _____**10.** Panic of 1837

a. informal group of trusted advisers relied on by President Andrew Jackson

b. vice president who declared that the states had the right to nullify any federal law with which they disagreed

c. practice of awarding government jobs to political supporters

d. belief that state power should be greater than federal power

e. political party made up of the supporters of Andrew Jackson for president in 1828

f. person who was the first Whig candidate to win the presidency

g. person who was chief justice of the Supreme Court when the Court supported the constitutionality of the Second Bank of the United States in the case of *McCulloch* v. *Maryland*

h. meetings to select a political party's presidential and vice presidential candidates

i. person who won the 1836 presidential election despite opposition from four candidates from the Whig Party

j. political organization formed in 1834 by a group of Jackson opponents

k. financial crisis that led to a severe economic depression

l. nickname given to an 1828 tariff by people who viewed the tariff as another example of the federal government's power over the states

Name _____ Class _____ Date _____

A New National Identity

★ ★

DAILY QUIZ 12.4

MULTIPLE CHOICE *10 points each* For each of the following, write the letter of the *best* choice in the space provided.

_____ 1. The Black Hawk War ended when
   a. the Americans surrendered to Sauk leader Black Hawk.
   b. the U.S. Army attacked the Sauk as they were attempting to retreat west across a river.
   c. Andrew Jackson signed a peace treaty with the Sauk.
   d. the Sauk agreed to oversee the Bureau of Indian Affairs.

_____ 2. Andrew Jackson and other officials wanted Indians in the Southwest to move to Indian Territory, an area containing most of present-day
   a. Oklahoma.
   b. California.
   c. Florida.
   d. Arizona.

_____ 3. The Treaty of Dancing Rabbit Creek, which ceded more than 10 million acres of land to the Americans, was signed by
   a. the Choctaw.
   b. the Sioux.
   c. the Comanche.
   d. the Cherokee.

_____ 4. Congress in 1830 passed the Indian Removal Act, which authorized the removal of Indians who lived
   a. in the Louisiana Territory.
   b. west of the Rocky Mountains.
   c. east of the Mississippi River.
   d. north of the Colorado River.

_____ 5. Sequoyah, a Cherokee, is well known for
   a. being the first American Indian appointed to the Supreme Court.
   b. introducing the horse into American culture.
   c. supporting the Indian Removal Act.
   d. creating a system of writing.

_____ 6. Even though the Cherokee adopted white culture, Georgia officials began preparing for the removal of the Cherokee after
   a. settlers asked the government to remove them.
   b. they refused to establish an election system.
   c. gold was discovered on their land.
   d. they refused to become U.S. citizens.

_____ 7. How did Georgia respond to the Supreme Court's ruling that removal of the Cherokee from the state was illegal?
   a. Georgia stopped its removal of the Cherokee.
   b. Georgia appealed the Court's ruling.
   c. Georgia defied the Court's ruling.
   d. Georgia withdrew from the Union.

_____ 8. Almost one fourth of the Cherokee died on an 800-mile forced march known as the
   a. Walk of Woe.
   b. Hike of Horrors.
   c. Road of Ruin.
   d. Trail of Tears.

_____ 9. Concerning their removal from their homeland, the Seminole of Florida
   a. resisted with armed force.
   b. went willingly to Indian Territory.
   c. appealed to the Supreme Court.
   d. tried to resist by adopting white culture.

_____ 10. Who led the Seminole in the Second Seminole War?
   a. John Ross
   b. Osceola
   c. Sequoyah
   d. Elias Boudinot

A New National Identity

★ ★

DAILY QUIZ 12.5

FILL IN THE BLANK *10 points each*   For each of the following statements, fill in the blank with the appropriate word, phrase, or name.

1. A biography of Revolutionary War hero _____ , written by William Wirt, was very popular despite the fact that Wirt had exaggerated some of the events in the book.

2. The writer _____ used satire to show Americans why they should learn from the past and be cautious about the future.

3. In the short story titled "_____ ," a man falls asleep for 20 years, during the time of the American Revolution, and wakes up to a society he does not recognize.

4. Although writer James Fenimore Cooper never saw the American frontier, he made the West and the _____ who lived there the focus of his novels.

5. By placing his fictional characters in real events, James Fenimore Cooper popularized a type of writing called _____ .

6. In 1822 Catharine Maria Sedgwick published her first novel, called _____ , which focused on the landscape and culture of her society.

7. Catharine Maria Sedgwick was the most successful female author of her time, and through her work she challenged commonly held notions about _____ .

8. A group of American artists called the _____ celebrated the beauty of the American landscape in their work, much of which focused on images from the Hudson River valley.

9. The painting *Fur Traders Descending the Missouri,* by the American artist George Caleb _____ , captures the rugged, lonely existence of fur traders in the West.

10. Before the Revolution most American architects followed the Georgian style used in Britain, but after the Revolution many American leaders called for architects to model their buildings after the style used in ancient _____ and _____ .

CHAPTER 13

Name _____ Class _____ Date _____

Industrial Growth in the North

★ ★

DAILY QUIZ 13.1

MATCHING *10 points each* Match each of the following people or terms with the correct description by writing the letter of the description in the space provided. Some descriptions will not be used.

_____ **1.** Industrial Revolution   _____ **6.** Hannah Slater

_____ **2.** textiles   _____ **7.** technology

_____ **3.** James Hargreaves   _____ **8.** Eli Whitney

_____ **4.** Richard Arkwright   _____ **9.** interchangeable parts

_____ **5.** Samuel Slater   _____ **10.** mass production

a. person who contributed to the success of the mill at Pawtucket, Rhode Island, by inventing cotton cloth for sewing, not weaving

b. person who began mass producing thousands of inexpensive clocks for American families in the early 1800s

c. cloth, the manufacture of which was one of the first breakthroughs of the Industrial Revolution

d. person who immigrated to the United States from Britain and formed a partnership to open a mill in Pawtucket, Rhode Island

e. inventor who promised to built 10,000 muskets for the U.S. government within a period of two years

f. period of rapid growth in the use of machines in manufacturing and production

g. efficient production of large numbers of identical goods

h. person who designed a small, inexpensive machine called the spinning jenny, which allowed a worker to make eight threads at the same time

i. person who tested Samuel Slater's knowledge of machinery and then formed a partnership with him and another man to open a mill

j. vital parts that go into making a product that are made in exactly the same way and thus can be used from product to product

k. tools used to produce goods or to do work

l. person who invented the water frame machine, which lowered the cost of cotton cloth and increased the speed of production

MULTIPLE CHOICE *10 points each* For each of the following, write the letter of the *best* choice in the space provided.

_____ 1. Samuel Slater, the mill owner, filled his labor needs at a low cost by
   a. using indentured servants.
   b. hiring entire families.
   c. using enslaved African Americans.
   d. hiring American Indian tribes.

_____ 2. The Rhode Island system, which was copied throughout America, consisted of
   a. using only young children to do mill work and paying the parents to farm.
   b. using the mill to produce both cloth and another product such as books.
   c. hiring families and dividing factory work into simple tasks.
   d. having the mill serve as both a factory for adults and a schoolroom for children.

_____ 3. Labor leader Sarah Bagley worked hard to achieve
   a. a 10-hour workday for workers.
   b. health insurance for workers.
   c. a two-week vacation for workers.
   d. a minimum wage for workers.

_____ 4. The first textile mill using the Lowell system was built in
   a. Waltham, Massachusetts, in 1813.
   b. Washington, D.C., in 1776.
   c. El Paso, Texas, in 1860.
   d. Philadelphia, Pennsylvania, in 1841.

_____ 5. Why did young women want to work at the Lowell mill?
   a. There were no other types of jobs available to women at that time.
   b. The advantages of mill work outweighed the disadvantages.
   c. They would be given ownership of their own mill after working at the Lowell mill for a period of 10 years.
   d. The mill paid them a higher wage than they could earn in other jobs.

_____ 6. Which of the following statements concerning the Lowell mill is correct?
   a. Workers worked an eight-hour day.
   b. The work was perfectly safe.
   c. Daily life was carefully regulated.
   d. Mill owners steadily decreased the size and speed of their machines.

_____ 7. Workers in the 1830s and 1840s began forming trade unions in order to
   a. provide education for workers.
   b. improve working conditions.
   c. trade manufactured goods for farm produce.
   d. trade goods with other countries.

_____ 8. Most early strikes by union members
   a. ended in the death of business owners.
   b. quickly resulted in changed laws.
   c. were not very successful.
   d. were composed totally of women.

_____ 9. What was the Lowell system?
   a. the combination of hiring young women and performing weaving and spinning in one mill
   b. the combination of hiring young children and using hand-powered looms in a series of small mills
   c. the use of poor families and hand-powered looms in one mill
   d. the use of indentured servants and water-powered looms in a series of small mills

_____ 10. At the time Sarah Bagley campaigned for labor reform, most workers worked
   a. seven days a week.
   b. 16 hours a day.
   c. 10 hours a day.
   d. six days a week.

Name _____ Class _____ Date _____

FILL IN THE BLANK *10 points each* For each of the following statements, fill in the blank with the appropriate word, phrase, or name.

1. In addition to the Industrial Revolution, the nation experienced a(n) _____ , a rapid growth in the speed and convenience of transportation during the 1800s.

2. Although several inventors in the United States and Europe had developed steam-powered boats in the late 1700s, the most successful person was _____ .

3. The *Clermont,* a full-sized commercial steamboat, created an immediate demand for a steamboat ferry service after it traveled up the _____ River without any trouble.

4. By 1840 there were over 500 steamboats in use on the _____ River.

5. To fill the need for fast ocean shipping, Americans introduced the _____ in the 1840s.

6. Steam-powered trains were first developed in the early 1800s in _____ .

7. American _____ raced his locomotive *Tom Thumb* against a horse-drawn railcar, but lost the race when the locomotive broke down near the end.

8. Railroad fever soon spread across the United States, and by 1840 U.S. railroad companies had laid some 1,000 more miles of track than existed in all of _____ .

9. By 1860 there were around _____ miles of railroad track linking almost every major city in the eastern United States.

10. When they were first introduced in the United States, locomotives were capable of going around _____ miles per hour while wagons often traveled less than 10 miles per hour.

TRUE/FALSE *10 points each*   Indicate whether each statement below is true or false by writing *T* or *F* in the space provided. If the statement is false, explain why.

_____**1.** Samuel Morse invented the telegraph.

_____

_____**2.** Morse code uses combinations of dots and dashes to represent each letter of the alphabet.

_____

_____**3.** By 1854 there were over 15,000 miles of telegraph cable connecting U.S. cities.

_____

_____**4.** As the Industrial Revolution progressed, more factory owners turned to water power instead of steam power to run their machinery.

_____

_____**5.** John Deere invented a plow with a steel blade that could easily slice through soil.

_____

_____**6.** Cyrus McCormick invented a mechanical reaper to cut down cotton quickly and easily.

_____

_____**7.** Deere's plow and McCormick's reaper made it possible for midwestern farmers to plant and harvest huge rice fields more cheaply.

_____

_____**8.** The most successful seller of sewing machines was Isaac Singer.

_____

_____**9.** Iceboxes cooled by large blocks of ice became available in the 1830s.

_____

_____**10.** As more cities developed public water systems, wealthy families were able to install water pumps inside their homes rather than rely on public pumps on street corners.

_____

Name _____ Class _____ Date _____

Agricultural Changes in the South

★ ★

DAILY QUIZ 14.1

MATCHING *10 points each* Match each of the following people or terms with the correct description by writing the letter of the description in the space provided. Some descriptions will not be used.

_____ **1.** John Rolfe   _____ **6.** Eli Whitney

_____ **2.** Thomas Jefferson   _____ **7.** cotton gin

_____ **3.** cotton   _____ **8.** planters

_____ **4.** China   _____ **9.** cotton belt

_____ **5.** West Indies   _____ **10.** scientific agriculture

a. origin of a type of cotton, yellow in color, that grew well in the backcountry of the Carolinas and Georgia but never became popular as a large-scale cash crop

b. person who in 1612 had introduced a high-grade tobacco that could be grown in Virginia

c. person who asked Eli Whitney for help in improving a machine that workers were using to remove the seeds from long-staple cotton

d. former U.S. president who believed that the entire future of the United States rested on agriculture

e. person who perfected a machine for removing short-staple seeds from cotton fibers

f. person who came to view slavery as "the most lawless and monstrous tyranny" and who ordered in his will that his slaves be freed

g. device that consisted of a cylinder filled with rows of wire teeth, the purpose of which was to remove short-staple seeds from cotton fibers

h. the use of scientific techniques to improve crop production

i. crop that some southerners thought might boost the economy when southern agriculture declined in the late 1700s

j. region of the country that grew most of the country's cotton

k. origin of long-staple cotton, which had long white fibers that could easily be removed from the seed

l. large-scale farmers who owned more than 20 slaves

Name _____ Class _____ Date _____

Agricultural Changes in the South

★ ★

DAILY QUIZ 14.2

TRUE/FALSE *10 points each*   Indicate whether each statement below is true or false by writing *T* or *F* in the space provided. If the statement is false, explain why.

_____**1.** France was the South's main foreign trading partner.

_____

_____**2.** Within the port cities of the South, crop brokers called factors managed the trade between planters and their customers.

_____

_____**3.** With the invention of the steam engine, steamboats became the main method by which farmers got their products to port cities.

_____

_____**4.** By 1850 the South possessed nearly 75 percent of the country's total canal mileage.

_____

_____**5.** Because cotton was so important to the southern economy, it was the only crop that southern farmers grew.

_____

_____**6.** The state of Louisiana was the capital of the U.S. sugar industry.

_____

_____**7.** As a result of the cotton boom, hemp and flax became major cash crops in some states.

_____

_____**8.** Most of the first factories in the South were built to process tobacco.

_____

_____**9.** The South relied on western states for all of its lumber needs.

_____

_____**10.** The Tredegar Iron Works was the only large factory in the South that made iron products.

_____

Agricultural Changes in the South

★ ★

DAILY QUIZ 14.3

MULTIPLE CHOICE *10 points each*   For each of the following, write the letter of the *best* choice in the space provided.

_____ **1.** In the first half of the 1800s, about how many white southern families owned slaves?
  a. one fourth
  b. one third
  c. one half
  d. all of them

_____ **2.** Male planters focused primarily on raising crops and left the running of the plantation household to
  a. their most trusted slaves.
  b. their wives.
  c. hired servants.
  d. indentured servants.

_____ **3.** Most white southerners were yeomen, meaning that they
  a. rented their land from planters.
  b. had college educations.
  c. moved to the South from the North.
  d. were small landowning farmers.

_____ **4.** Unlike the planters, yeomen
  a. worked side by side with slaves.
  b. paid their slaves a salary.
  c. freed their slaves after a certain amount of time had passed.
  d. refused to buy slaves.

_____ **5.** Which of the following was central to southern social life?
  a. charity work
  b. education
  c. religion
  d. politics

_____ **6.** What percentage of the southern population was made up of very poor landless whites?
  a. 10 percent
  b. 25 percent
  c. 50 percent
  d. 75 percent

_____ **7.** Which southern city attracted many writers who gathered to discuss their poems, short stories, and essays?
  a. Atlanta
  b. Charleston
  c. Miami
  d. New Orleans

_____ **8.** Much of the work in southern cities was done by
  a. urban business leaders.
  b. women.
  c. slaves.
  d. indentured servants.

_____ **9.** By 1860 more than half of all free African Americans lived in the
  a. North.
  b. West.
  c. Southwest.
  d. South.

_____ **10.** The center of social life for free urban African Americans was
  a. politics.
  b. the city library.
  c. the church.
  d. the schools.

Agricultural Changes in the South

★ ★

DAILY QUIZ 14.4

FILL IN THE BLANK *10 points each* For each of the following statements, fill in the blank with the appropriate word, phrase, or name.

1. On large plantations most slaves were assigned to specific jobs, with the majority of slaves working in the _____ .

2. Some plantation owners hired men called _____ to make sure that slaves followed orders and to carry out punishments.

3. Male and female slaves usually did the same work, as did enslaved children over the age of about _____ .

4. Most of the individuals who profited from slavery viewed slaves as _____ rather than as people.

5. The housing of most slaves consisted of dirt-floor _____ , which often had leaky roofs and few furnishings.

6. Many communities in the South passed strict slave _____ , which severely limited what slaves could do.

7. The most important unit of slave communities was the _____ , which made slaves fear being sold to another plantation.

8. Many slaves liked to tell _____ , or stories with a moral, which had lessons about how to survive under slavery.

9. Slaves expressed their religious beliefs in _____ , emotional Christian songs that blended African and European traditions.

10. A Virginia slave named _____ believed that God had called on him to overthrow slavery, and so he led a bloody revolt that ended in the death of nearly 60 white people in the area.

HRW material copyrighted under notice appearing earlier in this work.

★ ★

GEOGRAPHY AND HISTORY QUIZ

A Growing Economy

MULTIPLE CHOICE *10 points each* For each of the following, write the letter of the *best* choice in the space provided.

_____ **1.** The Fall Line is
    a. the line between rows of cotton where pickers could walk.
    b. an imaginary geographic line where river waters began flowing downhill.
    c. an imaginary line near factory machines behind which workers stood for safety.
    d. industrial products factory owners would have ready to sell in autumn.

_____ **2.** Which region of the United States developed an industrial economy?
    a. West
    b. Great Plains
    c. South
    d. North

_____ **3.** Industrial expansion was encouraged by
    a. the increased use of slave labor.
    b. improved communications networks.
    c. improved transportation networks.
    d. the invention of the cotton gin.

_____ **4.** Slavery was more common in areas of the South that grew
    a. wheat.
    b. cotton.
    c. corn.
    d. sugarcane.

_____ **5.** The cotton belt ran from
    a. Maryland to Florida.
    b. South Carolina to east Texas.
    c. North Carolina to South Carolina.
    d. Georgia to New Mexico.

_____ **6.** In 1860 the largest percentage of the nation's manufacturing establishments were located in the
    a. West.
    b. Midwest.
    c. South.
    d. Northeast.

_____ **7.** Where was tobacco an important agricultural product?
    a. West
    b. South
    c. Midwest
    d. Northwest

_____ **8.** Between 1790 and 1860, cotton production in the United States
    a. decreased steadily.
    b. stayed roughly the same.
    c. decreased until 1820 and then increased.
    d. increased steadily.

_____ **9.** Which of the following states produced the most cotton in 1860?
    a. Mississippi
    b. Tennessee
    c. Virginia
    d. South Carolina

_____ **10.** Between 1800 and 1860, the U.S. urban population grew most rapidly in the
    a. Northeast.
    b. Northwest.
    c. Midwest.
    d. South.

Name _____ Class _____ Date _____

TRUE/FALSE *10 points each*   Indicate whether each statement below is true or false by writing *T* or *F* in the space provided. If the statement is false, explain why.

_____ **1.** A period of widespread evangelism called the Second Great Revival began to emerge during the 1790s in towns across upstate New York and in the Ohio River valley.

_____

_____ **2.** The period of widespread evangelism appealed particularly to men.

_____

_____ **3.** One group of New England writers and thinkers sought spiritual inspiration from transcendentalism, the idea that people could rise above the material things in life.

_____

_____ **4.** The essay "Self-Reliance" was written by Henry David Thoreau.

_____

_____ **5.** Margaret Fuller's writings earned her the reputation as a champion of women's rights.

_____

_____ **6.** The Shakers, led by Mother Ann Lee, banned private property and lived a plain lifestyle.

_____

_____ **7.** Thomas Cole was a leading romantic painter and part of the Hudson River school.

_____

_____ **8.** One of the best-known examples of romantic literature is Edgar Allan Poe's novel, *The Scarlet Letter,* about Puritan society in the 1600s.

_____

_____ **9.** Many people consider *Moby Dick* to be one of the finest American novels ever written.

_____

_____ **10.** Henry Wadsworth Longfellow was the most popular poet of the mid-1800s.

_____

Name _____ Class _____ Date _____

FILL IN THE BLANK *10 points each* For each of the following statements, fill in the blank with the appropriate word, phrase, or name.

1. Between 1840 and 1860 more than 4 million immigrants came to the United States, with more than 3 million of them arriving from Ireland and _____ .

2. Many of the Irish who immigrated to the United States in the 1840s came to escape starvation in their country, which was caused by a _____ blight.

3. Germans were more likely than the Irish to become _____ and to live in rural areas where there was more land available, particularly in midwestern states.

4. Prior to the arrival of the new Catholic immigrants, most people who lived in the United States were _____ .

5. U.S. citizens who viewed immigrants with fear and suspicion and who were opposed to immigration were called _____ .

6. Members of the _____ Party wanted to exclude Catholics and foreigners from public office and to require immigrants to live in the United States for 21 years before they could become citizens.

7. U.S. cities grew rapidly during the mid-1800s, particularly in the Northeast and Middle Atlantic states, where three fourths of the nation's _____ jobs were located.

8. The families of Northeast merchants, manufacturers, professionals, and master craftspeople made up a growing _____ , which was a social and economic level between the wealthy and the poor.

9. Urban residents of the mid-1800s often lived in dirty, overcrowded, and poorly built housing called _____ .

10. The _____ epidemics of 1832 and 1849 in New York City hit Irish immigrants particularly hard.

Name _____ Class _____ Date _____

MULTIPLE CHOICE *10 points each* For each of the following, write the letter of the *best* choice in the space provided.

_____ **1.** The first co-educational college in the United States was
   a. Harvard College.
   b. Oberlin College.
   c. Princeton University.
   d. Yale University.

_____ **2.** The leaders of the reform efforts in the United States were members of the
   a. middle class.
   b. wealthiest class.
   c. working poor.
   d. poorest class.

_____ **3.** How did the common-school movement get its name?
   a. from the effort to ensure that all immigrant children received only enough basic education to hold jobs
   b. from the effort to ensure that all U.S. children shared a common curriculum
   c. from the nationwide effort to build all schools with a common architecture
   d. from the effort to have all children, regardless of class or background, educated in a common place

_____ **4.** Which of the following was the first college-level institution for women?
   a. The Catherine Beecher School
   b. Mount Holyoke Seminary
   c. Troy Female Seminary
   d. Oberlin College

_____ **5.** The leading voice for educational reform in the mid-1800s was
   a. William Holmes McGuffey.
   b. Josiah Quincy.
   c. Horace Mann.
   d. Lyman Beecher.

_____ **6.** The government of Massachusetts responded to Dorothea Dix's pleas by
   a. housing mentally ill people with criminals.
   b. ignoring her.
   c. having her arrested.
   d. creating separate facilities for people with mental illnesses.

_____ **7.** Americans' concerns about the negative effects of alcohol led to the growth of a(n)
   a. temperance movement.
   b. utopian movement.
   c. evangelical movement.
   d. transcendental movement.

_____ **8.** Dorothea Dix began a campaign to help people with mental illnesses after being outraged by the way they were treated at
   a. hospitals.
   b. jails.
   c. health clinics.
   d. schools.

_____ **9.** The first college to accept African Americans was
   a. Princeton University.
   b. Harvard College.
   c. Dartmouth College.
   d. Oberlin College.

_____ **10.** Thomas Gallaudet established
   a. the first free U.S. school for people with hearing impairments.
   b. the nation's first school for teacher training.
   c. a U.S. school for people with visual impairments.
   d. the first African American college in the United States.

★ ★

DAILY QUIZ 15.4

MATCHING *10 points each*   Match each of the following people or terms with the correct description by writing the letter of the description in the space provided. Some descriptions will not be used.

_____ **1.** abolition

_____ **2.** emancipation

_____ **3.** Quakers

_____ **4.** American Colonization Society

_____ **5.** Horace Greeley

_____ **6.** William Lloyd Garrison

_____ **7.** American Anti-Slavery Society

_____ **8.** Angelina Grimké

_____ **9.** Frederick Douglass

_____ **10.** Underground Railroad

a. person who published an antislavery newspaper, the *Liberator,* and helped found the American Anti-Slavery Society

b. group that established the colony of Liberia in Africa in 1822 for the resettlement of freed African Americans

c. one of the first groups, starting in colonial times, to challenge slavery on religious grounds

d. escaped slave who became the most famous conductor on the Underground Railroad

e. complete end to slavery

f. person who tried to bring southern women to the antislavery cause through publication of the pamphlet *Appeal to the Christian Women of the South*

g. term that means freedom from slavery

h. person who started the American Colonization Society

i. former slave who became one of the most important African American leaders of the 1800s

j. group that demanded immediate emancipation and racial equality for African Americans

k. network of people who arranged transportation and hiding places for escaped slaves

l. newspaper editor who became a strong voice for the abolitionist movement through the *New York Tribune*

Name _____ Class _____ Date _____

DAILY QUIZ 15.5

FILL IN THE BLANK *10 points each* For each of the following statements, fill in the blank with the appropriate word, phrase, or name.

1. Many women who had been active in the _____ movement also became active in the women's rights movement of the mid-1800s.

2. Activist _____ wrote and spoke about equal educational opportunities for women, identified laws that negatively affected women, and demanded equal pay for equal work.

3. Many activists were concerned that women could not vote or sit on juries and that married women in many states had little or no control over their own _____ .

4. When women attending the 1840 World Anti-Slavery Convention were forced to sit in a separate gallery of the assembly hall, abolitionist _____ sat with them, in protest of their exclusion from the proceedings.

5. In 1848 Elizabeth Cady Stanton and Lucretia Mott held the _____ in New York to organize a women's rights movement.

6. The organizers of the convention wrote a _____ , modeled on the language of the Declaration of Independence, which detailed their beliefs about social injustice against women.

7. More than _____ people attended the women's rights convention in Seneca Falls, New York.

8. Activist _____ encouraged women to keep their maiden names when they married.

9. Quaker _____ argued that women and men should receive equal pay for equal work and that women should be allowed to enter traditionally male professions such as religion and law.

10. In 1860 the state legislature of _____ passed a law giving married women ownership of their wages and property.

CHAPTER

16

Expanding West

★ ★

DAILY QUIZ 16.1

TRUE/FALSE *10 points each*   Indicate whether each statement below is true or false by writing *T* or *F* in the space provided. If the statement is false, explain why.

_____**1.** In California, missions were the center of colonial society.

_____

_____**2.** Most of the labor in California was done by indentured servants living on mission lands under the control of Franciscan priests.

_____

_____**3.** Spanish colonists in California, known as Americos, were basically cut off from the rest of New Spain because of the great distance.

_____

_____**4.** Pueblo Indians and Spanish colonists in New Mexico heavily influenced one another.

_____

_____**5.** Spanish settlers in Texas, known as Tejanos, developed a cattle-ranching society.

_____

_____**6.** Spanish expansion in Texas was limited by the English settlers already living there.

_____

_____**7.** A rebellion in Mexico begun by Father Hidalgo ended in Mexico becoming an independent nation in 1821 and a republic in 1824.

_____

_____**8.** In 1833 Mexican officials ended the mission system, giving mission lands to Californios.

_____

_____**9.** After Mexican independence, Texas became part of the province of Coahuila y Tejas.

_____

_____**10.** After Mexico's war for independence, few Tejanos were left in Texas.

_____

Name _____ Class _____ Date _____

★ ★

DAILY QUIZ 16.2

MATCHING *10 points each*   Match each of the following people or terms with the correct description by writing the letter of the description in the space provided. Some descriptions will not be used.

_____**1.** James Long

_____**2.** *empresarios*

_____**3.** Stephen F. Austin

_____**4.** African Americans

_____**5.** Antonio López de Santa Anna

_____**6.** Gonzales

_____**7.** San Antonio

_____**8.** Goliad

_____**9.** Sam Houston

_____**10.** San Jacinto

a. person who suspended the Mexican Constitution of 1824 after he became the new Mexican leader

b. person who persuaded a group of U.S. citizens from Natchez, Mississippi, to settle illegally in Spanish Mexico and build a fort on Galveston Bay

c. person chosen to serve as commander in chief of the newly formed Texas army

d. town in which a group of Texans led by William Travis and Jim Bowie defended the Alamo against Santa Anna and his troops

e. people brought to Texas by southern settlers to work the land, often growing cotton

f. agents contracted by Mexico to bring settlers to Texas in exchange for a large amount of land

g. person who became known as the Angel of Goliad after hiding and saving the lives of several Texas rebels sentenced to death after the Battle of Goliad

h. person who selected a colony site on the lower Colorado River and brought 300 families, known as the Old Three Hundred, to Texas

i. person chosen by the delegates at the Convention of 1836 to be temporary president of Texas

j. town in which a battle between Mexican forces and Texas troops resulted in the surrender and execution of Commander James Fannin and almost 400 of his soldiers

k. scene of the battle in which Santa Anna's army was destroyed by Texas troops and Santa Anna was captured

l. town in which the first battle of the Texas Revolution took place

FILL IN THE BLANK *10 points each*   For each of the following statements, fill in the blank with the appropriate word, phrase, or name.

1. The independent nation of Texas was called the Republic of Texas, and its capital was the new town of _____ .

2. One of the new Texas government's first decisions was whether to ask the United States to _____ , or take control of, Texas.

3. President Andrew Jackson was concerned that adding Texas as a _____ state would upset the balance between free states and slave states.

4. When Mirabeau Lamar became president of the Texas republic in 1838, he demanded that _____ leave their homelands and follow all Texas laws, or face military action.

5. The Republic of Texas encouraged immigration from the United States and Europe by offering _____ to settlers.

6. In 1839 the capital of Texas was moved from Houston to _____ .

7. In 1840 Texas passed a law forcing most _____ to leave the republic.

8. The largest group of European immigrants to Texas came from various regions of what is now _____ .

9. Although the Texas republic was rich in resources, particularly _____ , it had little cash and was almost bankrupt.

10. When _____ returned to the presidency in 1841, he tried to end the fighting between Mexico and Texas, finally signing a peace agreement with Santa Anna in 1844.

MULTIPLE CHOICE *10 points each*   For each of the following, write the letter of the *best* choice in the space provided.

_____ **1.** Most of the first non-Indians who traveled to the Rocky Mountains and the Pacific Northwest were
  a. farmers.
  b. fur traders and trappers.
  c. lumberjacks.
  d. hunters and fishers.

_____ **2.** The rendezvous was a(n)
  a. annual meeting of the mountain men.
  b. Indian wedding custom.
  c. fur-trading post at the mouth of the Columbia River.
  d. agreement among a group of missionaries to bring Christianity to the far western frontier.

_____ **3.** Marcus and Narcissa Whitman traveled to the Pacific Northwest in 1836 to
  a. search for gold.
  b. open a trading post.
  c. convert Indians to Christianity.
  d. open a school for the children of mountain men.

_____ **4.** About how long did it take pioneers to reach Oregon Country?
  a. two to four months
  b. six to eight months
  c. ten months to a year
  d. two to three years

_____ **5.** Which country signed the 1819 Adams-Onís Treaty with the United States to settle claims to Oregon Country?
  a. Britain
  b. Russia
  c. Spain
  d. France

_____ **6.** Britain's main interest in Oregon Country and the Pacific Northwest was
  a. fur.
  b. gold.
  c. lumber.
  d. silver.

_____ **7.** The demand for beaver pelts decreased as
  a. they became too costly.
  b. clothing fashions changed.
  c. westerners began keeping beavers as pets.
  d. people came to believe that killing beavers was morally wrong.

_____ **8.** Some of the settlers who stayed with Marcus and Narcissa Whitman in Oregon Country carried diseases that harmed the
  a. Cherokee.
  b. Comanche.
  c. Cheyenne.
  d. Cayuse.

_____ **9.** About how much money did a family of four need to buy supplies for the journey to Oregon Country?
  a. $200
  b. $600
  c. $2,000
  d. $6,000

_____ **10.** Who was John Jacob Astor?
  a. a well-known mountain man
  b. a missionary in Oregon Country
  c. an Indian guide who led farmers, miners, and ranchers to the West
  d. a merchant who bought furs from trappers

Expanding West

★ ★

DAILY QUIZ 16.5

TRUE/FALSE *10 points each*   Indicate whether each statement below is true or false by writing *T* or *F* in the space provided. If the statement is false, explain why.

_____**1.** The branch of the Oregon Trail leading to California became known as the California Trail.

_____

_____**2.** All members of the Donner party froze to death in the Sierra Nevada.

_____

_____**3.** Swiss immigrant John Sutter received permission from French officials to build a colony named Sutter's Fort near the Sacramento River.

_____

_____**4.** Sutter's Fort soon became a popular destination for many U.S. immigrants.

_____

_____**5.** The Santa Fe Trail, which ran from Independence, Missouri, to Santa Fe, New Mexico, was established by American merchants.

_____

_____**6.** The U.S. government did nothing to help protect traders on the Santa Fe Trail.

_____

_____**7.** Susan Shelby Magoffin was one of the first white women to travel on the Santa Fe Trail.

_____

_____**8.** El Camino Real, or King's Road, still connected Santa Fe to Mexico City.

_____

_____**9.** Portrait painter George Catlin went west to paint scenes of American Indians.

_____

_____**10.** The work of frontier artists has only recently become popular.

_____

FILL IN THE BLANK *10 points each*   For each of the following statements, fill in the blank with the appropriate word, phrase, or name.

1. South Carolina senator _____ believed that if the United States was patient and avoided unnecessary wars, it would eventually become the strongest nation in the world.

2. By the 1840s many Americans believed that the United States was meant to expand across the continent to the _____ and that nothing could stop this growth from taking place.

3. The idea that the United States was meant to occupy the continent from ocean to ocean came to be known as _____ .

4. Most supporters of the expansion of the United States ignored the fact that thousands of _____ and Mexicans had been living in the West for centuries.

5. President John Tyler believed that the annexation of _____ would help the South by adding another slave state to the nation.

6. _____ strongly disagreed with the United States over where in Oregon to draw the U.S.-Canada border.

7. In 1846 the United States and Britain signed a treaty that gave the United States all _____ land south of the 49th parallel.

8. Texas, whose annexation by the United States angered the _____ government, became a U.S. state in December 1845.

9. Mexico rejected the Texas and U.S. claim that the Rio Grande marked the southern border of Texas and instead claimed that the real border lay along the _____ River, many miles to the north.

10. After Mexican soldiers attacked a group of U.S. soldiers at the Rio Grande, President _____ urged Congress to declare war on Mexico.

Name _____ Class _____ Date _____

Manifest Destiny and War

★ ★

DAILY QUIZ 17.2

MATCHING *10 points each* Match each of the following people or terms with the correct description by writing the letter of the description in the space provided. Some descriptions will not be used.

_____**1.** Henry David Thoreau   _____**6.** Winfield Scott

_____ **2.** Ralph Waldo Emerson   _____**7.** Nicholas Trist

_____ **3.** Zachary Taylor   _____**8.** Treaty of Guadalupe Hidalgo

_____ **4.** Stephen Kearny   _____**9.** Mexican Cession

_____ **5.** Bear Flag Revolt   _____**10.** Gadsden Purchase

a. U.S. general whose soldiers fought and won battles with the Mexicans south of the Nueces River, at Palo Alto and Resaca de la Palma on May 8 and 9, 1846

b. revolt against Californios by a small group of Americans near Sonoma, who declared California to be an independent republic

c. transcendentalist writer who was so upset by the war that he went to jail rather than pay taxes, which he thought would be used to support the fighting in Mexico

d. government body that supported President's Polk's war message and that issued a statement saying that the war was started by the Republic of Mexico

e. U.S. State Department official who was assigned by President Polk to negotiate a peace treaty with Mexico

f. land acquired by the United States at the end of the Mexican War, including the present-day states of California, Nevada, and Utah, most of Arizona and New Mexico, and parts of Colorado, Wyoming, and the area claimed by Texas north of the Rio Grande

g. transcendentalist who predicted that the disagreements over the Mexican War would divide Americans

h. U.S. general, known to the troops as Old Fuss and Feathers, who ordered a massive assault on Mexico City

i. area of land bought by the United States from Mexico that included the southern parts of present-day Arizona and New Mexico

j. young Whig congressman who questioned whether the fighting had really started on U.S. soil

k. 1848 agreement in which the United States received much of Mexico's northern territory

l. U.S. general who took the city of Santa Fe without a fight, claimed the entire territory of New Mexico for the United States, and prepared to march to California

TRUE/FALSE *10 points each* Indicate whether each statement below is true or false by writing *T* or *F* in the space provided. If the statement is false, explain why.

_____ **1.** The U.S. government often forced Mexican American landowners to go to court to prove that they had a title to their land.

_____

_____ **2.** Mexican American landholders faced problems because Mexican legal concepts such as community property or community water rights were ignored by new settlers.

_____

_____ **3.** American settlers often tried to seize valuable grazing land from southwestern Indians.

_____

_____ **4.** In settlements with large Mexican populations, laws were printed only in Spanish.

_____

_____ **5.** Place-names throughout the Southwest reflect the region's French heritage.

_____

_____ **6.** Adobe, a building material first developed by the Pueblo Indians and then adopted by the Spanish, was rejected by American settlers in New Mexico and California.

_____

_____ **7.** Americans brought manufactured goods and capital to the Southwest.

_____

_____ **8.** Mormons are members of the Church of Jesus Christ of Latter-Day Saints.

_____

_____ **9.** The Mormon practice of polygamy made Mormons the target of persecution.

_____

_____ **10.** Joseph Smith chose present-day Idaho as the final destination for the Mormons.

_____

Name _____ Class _____ Date _____

DAILY QUIZ 17.4

MULTIPLE CHOICE *10 points each* For each of the following, write the letter of the *best* choice in the space provided.

_____ **1.** The people who rushed to California to search for gold were known as
   a. twenty-niners.
   b. thirty-niners.
   c. forty-niners.
   d. fifty-niners.

_____ **2.** How many years after it was acquired by the United States did California become eligible for statehood?
   a. two years
   b. four years
   c. eight years
   d. ten years

_____ **3.** Whatever their method of travel to California, most gold-seekers arrived in
   a. Los Angeles.
   b. Sacramento.
   c. San Diego.
   d. San Francisco.

_____ **4.** The most popular mining method used by prospectors was
   a. placer mining.
   b. diverting streams and rivers.
   c. digging shafts and tunnels.
   d. blasting with dynamite.

_____ **5.** Chinese immigrants who came to the West to make their fortunes were known as *gam saan haak,* or
   a. "nomads to Nowhere Bound."
   b. "wanderers to Fools' Hill."
   c. "travelers to Gold Mountain."
   d. "voyagers to Useless Rock."

_____ **6.** In 1852 California placed a high monthly tax on
   a. all foreign miners.
   b. the value of miners' gold strikes.
   c. the amount of water consumed.
   d. all landowners.

_____ **7.** Most of the miners in California were
   a. young, married men.
   b. middle-aged, married men.
   c. young, unmarried men.
   d. middle-aged, widowed men.

_____ **8.** Which of the following immigrants were not allowed to become U.S. citizens?
   a. Japanese
   b. Chinese
   c. Irish
   d. German

_____ **9.** Like most of the U.S. gold-seekers, foreign prospectors
   a. intended to return home after they had made their fortunes.
   b. got rich overnight.
   c. used dynamite to blast on a daily basis.
   d. brought their families with them to California.

_____ **10.** Nearly 80 percent of those who went to California in search of gold were
   a. Spanish.
   b. American.
   c. French.
   d. British.

Name _____ Class _____ Date _____

★ ★

GEOGRAPHY AND HISTORY QUIZ

Westward Expansion

FILL IN THE BLANK *10 points each* For each of the following statements, fill in the blank with the appropriate word, phrase, or name.

1. After the United States annexed _____ in 1845, Mexico bitterly disputed that territory's southern and western boundary claims and argued that the land in those areas legally belonged to Mexico.

2. The population of Texas grew from 30,000 in 1836 to 140,000 in 1846, mainly as a result of _____ from the United States.

3. Before they made their 1846 agreement on a boundary line dividing Canada and Oregon, both the United States and _____ laid claim to the Oregon Country.

4. The most populated and economically developed of the Mexican territories that became a part of the United States was _____ .

5. The rapid increase in California's population, which was triggered by the gold rush that began in the late 1840s, led to a large decline in the percentage of Californians that were _____ .

6. Today, the largest concentration of Hispanic Americans can be found in the _____ region of the United States.

7. The _____ has the most diverse population of any region in the United States at the present time.

8. In every region of the United States, _____ make up the smallest percentage of the population.

9. Most immigrants to the United States in 1850 came from _____ .

10. The largest percentage of immigrants to the United States in 1994 came from _____ .

Name _____ Class _____ Date _____

MATCHING *10 points each* Match each of the following people or terms with the correct description by writing the letter of the description in the space provided. Some descriptions will not be used.

_____ **1.** Wilmot Proviso

_____ **2.** sectionalism

_____ **3.** popular sovereignty

_____ **4.** Free-Soil Party

_____ **5.** Henry Clay

_____ **6.** Compromise of 1850

_____ **7.** Fugitive Slave Act

_____ **8.** Anthony Burns

_____ **9.** *Uncle Tom's Cabin*

_____ **10.** Harriet Beecher Stowe

a. person who introduced a proposal to prohibit slavery in all parts of the territory won by the United States during the Mexican War

b. person who offered a series of proposals to address all of the current issues of sectional disagreement

c. series of decisions that seemed to be a final settlement of the slavery controversy

d. devotion to the interests of one region instead of to the country as a whole

e. powerful antislavery novel

f. fugitive slave from Virginia who was arrested and jailed in Boston, where a group of abolitionists unsuccessfully tried to rescue him

g. principle that would allow voters in a particular territory to decide whether they wanted to ban or permit slavery

h. law that made it a federal crime to assist runaway slaves and allowed slaves to be arrested even in areas where slavery was illegal

i. political party that endorsed the Wilmot Proviso and that chose former president Martin Van Buren of New York as their candidate for president

j. person who wrote *Uncle Tom's Cabin*

k. proposal that stated that neither slavery nor involuntary servitude would ever exist in any part of the Mexican Cession

l. president who signed each bill that made up the Compromise of 1850

Name _____ **Class** _____ **Date** _____

A Divided Nation

★ ★

DAILY QUIZ 18.2

TRUE/FALSE _10 points each_   Indicate whether each statement below is true or false by writing _T_ or _F_ in the space provided. If the statement is false, explain why.

_____**1.** Franklin Pierce swore to honor the Compromise of 1850 and enforce the Fugitive Slave Act.

_____

_____**2.** The 1854 Kansas-Nebraska Act divided the remainder of the Louisiana Purchase into two territories in which the slavery question would be decided by popular sovereignty.

_____

_____**3.** With popular sovereignty to determine the status of slavery in Nebraska, antislavery and pro-slavery groups both worked to get people to Nebraska as quickly as possible.

_____

_____**4.** By 1856 Nebraska had both a pro-slavery government and an antislavery government.

_____

_____**5.** Antislavery settlers in Kansas were known as free-soilers.

_____

_____**6.** Reverend Henry Ward Beecher sent rifles to help the cause of the Kansas free-soilers.

_____

_____**7.** The Sack of Lawrence occurred when a free-soil posse sent to arrest pro-slavery leaders took out its anger on the town of Lawrence.

_____

_____**8.** John Brown and seven others killed five pro-slavery men in the Pottawatomie Massacre.

_____

_____**9.** After the Pottawatomie Massacre, Nebraska collapsed into a state of civil war.

_____

_____**10.** Representative Preston Brooks beat Senator Charles Sumner unconscious with a cane.

_____

FILL IN THE BLANK *10 points each* For each of the following statements, fill in the blank with the appropriate word, phrase, or name.

1. The _____ Party was formed in 1854 by people opposed to the recently passed Kansas-Nebraska Act.

2. When the _____ became public in March 1855, many northerners criticized the Democrats' attempt to acquire more slave territory.

3. The _____ Party fell apart completely because of the Kansas-Nebraska bill.

4. The main goal of the Republican Party was to prevent the spread of _____ to the West, which to the public made the Republicans a "single-issue party."

5. The Know-Nothing Party chose _____ as their presidential candidate in the election of 1856.

6. On election day, Democrat _____ carried 14 of the 15 slave states and beat out his opponents to become the new president.

7. In the *Dred Scott* decision, the Supreme Court concluded that African Americans, whether slave or free, were not citizens under the U.S. _____ .

8. The Supreme Court also ruled that since slaves were considered _____ , Congress could not prohibit someone from taking slaves into a federal territory.

9. The central issue of the seven _____ debates held in Illinois in 1858 involved slavery and its future in the West.

10. In the _____ , Stephen Douglas explained how, if Congress could not ban slavery from a federal territory, Congress could allow the citizens of that territory to ban it.

★ ★ ★ ★ ★ ★ ★ ★ ★ ★ ★ ★ ★ ★ ★ ★ ★ ★ ★

DAILY QUIZ 18.4

MULTIPLE CHOICE *10 points each* For each of the following, write the letter of the *best* choice in the space provided.

_____ **1.** The purpose of the raid on Harpers Ferry was to
   a. kidnap slaves and take them to the South.
   b. aid the abolitionists' cause.
   c. seek revenge for the Pottawatomie Massacre.
   d. sack the town as Lawrence had been sacked.

_____ **2.** Who led the raid on Harpers Ferry?
   a. John Brown
   b. Robert E. Lee
   c. Stephen Douglas
   d. Jefferson Davis

_____ **3.** At his trial, the leader of the raid on Harpers Ferry was
   a. found not guilty and released.
   b. sentenced to pay a fine of $1,000.
   c. sentenced to life in prison.
   d. sentenced to death.

_____ **4.** The first state to secede from the Union was
   a. South Carolina.
   b. North Carolina.
   c. Virginia.
   d. New Hampshire.

_____ **5.** Which of the following statements about the 1860 presidential election is correct?
   a. Stephen Douglas received the highest number of electoral votes.
   b. Stephen Douglas had the lowest number of overall popular votes.
   c. Abraham Lincoln won nearly 100 percent of the overall popular vote.
   d. Abraham Lincoln did not carry a single southern state.

_____ **6.** Just four days after Lincoln's election,
   a. Congress passed a law abolishing slavery in the South.
   b. Stephen Douglas called for a recount of the election votes.
   c. South Carolina called for a special convention to consider secession.
   d. New York's legislature voted to withdraw the state from the Union.

_____ **7.** What was the outcome of the Crittenden Compromise?
   a. Every Republican in the Senate approved it.
   b. Every Democrat in the House of Representatives rejected it.
   c. Every Republican in the Senate rejected it.
   d. It was approved by the Senate but rejected by the House.

_____ **8.** What new political party was formed during the presidential campaign of 1860?
   a. Whig Party
   b. Constitutional Union Party
   c. Free-Soilers Party
   d. Republican Party

_____ **9.** In 1861 delegates from the seceding states met to form a new nation, called
   a. the Secession States of America.
   b. the Confederate States of America.
   c. the United States of the South.
   d. the Confederate States of the Union.

_____ **10.** In 1861 Jefferson Davis was elected
   a. president of the Confederacy.
   b. chief justice of the Supreme Court.
   c. vice president of the United States.
   d. president of the U.S. Senate.

★ ★

DAILY QUIZ 19.1

FILL IN THE BLANK *10 points each*   For each of the following statements, fill in the blank with the appropriate word, phrase, or name.

1. Before President-elect Abraham Lincoln took office, _____ states had seceded from the Union.

2. In April 1861 Union forces surrendered _____ , an important federal outpost in the South, to the Confederates.

3. The states of the Upper South—Virginia, North Carolina, and Tennessee—all joined the _____ soon after Abraham Lincoln made a request for troops.

4. The new capital of the Confederacy, _____ , Virginia, replaced the former capital of Montgomery, Alabama.

5. The strategic position of Delaware, Kentucky, Missouri, and Maryland, which together were known as _____ , made them vital to both the North and the South.

6. A new state called _____ was created after President Lincoln sent troops into western Virginia, encouraging the region's largely pro-Union population to refuse to join the Confederacy.

7. The U.S. _____ , created in June 1861, sent bandages, medicines, and food to Union army camps and hospitals.

8. Most of the nation's factories were located in the _____ .

9. Part of Union general Winfield Scott's military strategy involved gaining control of the _____ River, which would divide the Confederacy and cut its internal communications.

10. The main Confederate offensive plan focused on seizing _____ .

★ ★

DAILY QUIZ 19.2

MULTIPLE CHOICE *10 points each* For each of the following, write the letter of the *best* choice in the space provided.

_____ **1.** The first major clash of Union and Confederate forces took place at the
  a. Battle of Antietam.
  b. Second Battle of Bull Run.
  c. First Battle of Bull Run.
  d. Seven Days' Battles.

_____ **2.** General Lee forced General McClellan to retreat from the Richmond area during the
  a. Second Battle of Bull Run.
  b. Battle of Antietam.
  c. Seven Days' Battles.
  d. First Battle of Bull Run.

_____ **3.** The Union troops at the First Battle of Bull Run were forced into retreat by Confederate forces led by General
  a. Stonewall Jackson.
  b. Irvin McDowell.
  c. Robert E. Lee.
  d. George B. McClellan.

_____ **4.** By the end of August 1862 General Lee's forces had pushed most of their opponents out of
  a. Alabama.
  b. Washington.
  c. Virginia.
  d. Mississippi.

_____ **5.** President Lincoln sent Union troops back into Virginia in the spring of 1862 because he wanted to
  a. force Virginia and West Virginia to merge into one Union state.
  b. gain control of the Mississippi River.
  c. defeat the Confederates' Indian allies.
  d. capture the Confederate capital of Richmond.

_____ **6.** Which of the following was the bloodiest single-day battle in U.S. military history?
  a. First Battle of Bull Run
  b. Battle of Antietam
  c. Second Battle of Bull Run
  d. Seven Days' Battles

_____ **7.** The Confederacy introduced a new, heavily armored type of warship known as a(n)
  a. steel trap.
  b. ironclad.
  c. bronze bomber.
  d. copperclad.

_____ **8.** Which of the following people had declined President Lincoln's 1861 request to take command of Union forces?
  a. Robert E. Lee
  b. Joseph Johnston
  c. Jeb Stuart
  d. George B. McClellan

_____ **9.** Which of the following statements is correct?
  a. The Confederates controlled the sea.
  b. The Union was in no position to conduct naval warfare.
  c. Most naval officers were loyal to the Confederacy.
  d. The Union controlled the sea.

_____ **10.** Which of the following warships saved the Union fleet and ensured the continuation of the Union's blockade?
  a. the *Monitor*
  b. the *Washington*
  c. the *Merrimack*
  d. the *Virginia*

Name _____ Class _____ Date _____

CHAPTER 19

The Civil War

★ ★

DAILY QUIZ 19.3

TRUE/FALSE *10 points each* Indicate whether each statement below is true or false by writing *T* or *F* in the space provided. If the statement is false, explain why.

_____ **1.** The Confederate strategy in the West focused on controlling the Mississippi River.

_____

_____ **2.** Ulysses S. Grant was the most important figure in the western theater of war.

_____

_____ **3.** The Union capture of Fort Henry and Fort Donelson secured Union control of Kentucky and much of Tennessee.

_____

_____ **4.** Although the Battle of Shiloh initially caught General Grant by surprise, Union reinforcements forced the Confederates to retreat.

_____

_____ **5.** David Farragut easily destroyed the two forts guarding the approach to New Orleans.

_____

_____ **6.** Following the Union capture of New Orleans, Commodore Farragut sailed farther up the Mississippi River, taking Baton Rouge, Louisiana, and Natchez, Mississippi.

_____

_____ **7.** The Confederate defenders of Vicksburg easily defeated the Union forces.

_____

_____ **8.** The capture of Vicksburg gave the Union complete control of the Mississippi.

_____

_____ **9.** Union forces defeated pro-Confederate Missourians in the Battle of Pea Ridge.

_____

_____ **10.** In the Battle of Pea Ridge, Union forces were helped by a group of American Indians.

_____

HRW material copyrighted under notice appearing earlier in this work.

Call to Freedom ★ Daily Quizzes **87**

Name _____ Class _____ Date _____

DAILY QUIZ 19.4

MATCHING *10 points each* Match each of the following people or terms with the correct description by writing the letter of the description in the space provided. Some descriptions will not be used.

_____**1.** Emancipation Proclamation   _____**6.** Copperheads

_____ **2.** William Lloyd Garrison   _____**7.** *habeas corpus*

_____ **3.** Frederick Douglass   _____**8.** draft

_____ **4.** contrabands   _____**9.** Clara Barton

_____ **5.** 54th Massachusetts Infantry   _____**10.** Andersonville

a. African American Union regiment that played a key role in the capture of Fort Wagner in South Carolina

b. person who served as head of the more than 3,000 nurses who took care of Union soldiers

c. order that called for all slaves in areas rebelling against the Union to be freed

d. name that northern Democrats opposed to the war were called by their enemies

e. person whose volunteer medical efforts formed the basis for what would later become the American Red Cross

f. abolitionist who celebrated the Emancipation Proclamation

g. name that northern Democrats opposed to the war called themselves

h. escaped slaves, authorized by President Lincoln to enlist in the Union army

i. military prisoner-of-war camp that had the worst conditions of any prison camp in the war

j. constitutional protection against unlawful imprisonment

k. abolitionist who believed that the Emancipation Proclamation did not go far enough

l. law that in the South excluded those who owned a large number of slaves, causing resentment among poor southerners

Name _____ Class _____ Date _____

FILL IN THE BLANK *10 points each* For each of the following statements, fill in the blank with the appropriate word, phrase, or name.

1. On the first day of the Battle of Gettysburg, Confederate forces pushed the Union line back to _____ , just south of the town of Gettysburg.

2. General Lee planned to charge the center of the Union line using three divisions of Confederate soldiers, the largest under the command of General _____ .

3. The _____ victory at the Battle of Gettysburg, combined with General Grant's capture of Vicksburg on the same day, renewed northern confidence that the war could be won.

4. In the _____ , President Lincoln spoke of what the Battle of Gettysburg meant to the soldiers who fought it and to the Union they represented.

5. Impressed with the successes of General _____ in the West, President Lincoln transferred him to the eastern theater and made him supreme commander of the Union armies.

6. General _____ carried out a Union strategy to destroy southern railroads and industries.

7. The city of _____ , Georgia, fell to Union forces on September 2, 1864, depriving the South of a vital railroad junction and center of industry.

8. On his March to the Sea, General Sherman engaged in _____ —targeting civilian as well as military resources to destroy an opponent's economy and ability to fight.

9. Trapped west of Richmond in the town of _____ , General Lee concluded that there was nothing left to do but surrender.

10. After receiving assurances from General Grant that Confederate troops would be allowed to keep their horses and that they would not be tried for _____ , General Lee signed the surrender documents.

UNIT
8

Name _____ Class _____ Date _____

GEOGRAPHY AND HISTORY QUIZ

Theaters of War

TRUE/FALSE *20 points each* Indicate whether each statement below is true or false by writing *T* or *F* in the space provided. If the statement is false, explain why.

_____ **1.** Because the population of the North was more than twice as large as that of the South, the Union was able to put more soldiers in the field.

_____

_____ **2.** To the dismay of Confederate leaders, Britain and France decided that their need for southern cotton was not great enough to openly support the Confederacy in its war efforts.

_____

_____ **3.** The commanders of the Confederate army planned to cut off Arkansas, Louisiana, and Texas by taking control of the Mississippi River.

_____

_____ **4.** The capture of Chattanooga, Tennessee, was important to the Union forces because the railroad lines along which the city was located connected the eastern and western parts of the Confederacy.

_____

_____ **5.** Florida, which was badly damaged during General Sherman's March to the Sea, saw the total value of its farms cut in half after the Civil War.

_____

★ ★

DAILY QUIZ 20.1

MULTIPLE CHOICE *10 points each*   For each of the following, write the letter of the *best* choice in the space provided.

_____ **1.** The Freedmen's Bureau was created by
   a. President Andrew Johnson.
   b. the Supreme Court.
   c. President Abraham Lincoln.
   d. Congress.

_____ **2.** Following the war, freedpeople did all of the following *EXCEPT*
   a. hold ceremonies to legalize marriages not recognized under slavery.
   b. take new last names.
   c. search for their relatives.
   d. move from mostly black counties to places with more white people.

_____ **3.** President Andrew Johnson's plan for Reconstruction
   a. pardoned all northerners who took a loyalty oath and accepted slavery.
   b. required southern states to accept a constitution written by Congress.
   c. won instant congressional approval.
   d. was similar in many ways to Lincoln's Ten-Percent Plan.

_____ **4.** The Thirteenth Amendment
   a. outlawed civil wars within the boundaries of the United States.
   b. created the death penalty for people who assassinated a U.S. president.
   c. made slavery illegal throughout the United States.
   d. gave amnesty to all southerners.

_____ **5.** The Emancipation Proclamation
   a. was declared illegal in 1865.
   b. made it illegal for northerners to discriminate against southerners.
   c. had freed slaves only in the Confederate states that had been unoccupied by Union forces.
   d. abolished the Thirteenth Amendment.

_____ **6.** After the Civil War,
   a. life for southerners was exactly as it was before the Civil War.
   b. southerners had to deal with farms and cities that had been destroyed.
   c. southerners found it easier to travel because Union troops had built railroads throughout the South.
   d. banks thrived because Confederate money was accepted everywhere.

_____ **7.** At its high point the Freedmen's Bureau had about 900 agents to help
   a. African Americans in the North.
   b. all poor people in the South.
   c. poor white people in the South.
   d. poor white people in the North.

_____ **8.** One of the greatest successes of the Freedmen's Bureau was in
   a. creating public schools in the South.
   b. finding northern factory jobs for all freedpeople who wanted them.
   c. helping freedpeople who wished to move to other countries.
   d. helping freedpeople keep land given to them by the U.S. government.

_____ **9.** Abraham Lincoln was assassinated by
   a. John Wilkes Booth.
   b. Alexander Stephens.
   c. Benjamin Wade.
   d. Gideon Welles.

_____ **10.** Benjamin Wade and Henry Davis disagreed with Abraham Lincoln on
   a. whether or not freedpeople should be permitted to move to other states.
   b. how best to bring the southern states back into the Union.
   c. how to encourage white planters to give up their land to freedpeople.
   d. whether slavery should be abolished.

★ ★

DAILY QUIZ 20.2

TRUE/FALSE *10 points each* Indicate whether each statement below is true or false by writing *T* or *F* in the space provided. If the statement is false, explain why.

_____ **1.** Shortly after the end of the Civil War, every southern state passed Black Codes.

_____

_____ **2.** Black Codes were designed to help African Americans economically.

_____

_____ **3.** Radical Republicans considered the Black Codes to be undemocratic and cruel.

_____

_____ **4.** President Andrew Johnson vetoed a bill that would have allowed military courts to try individuals accused of violating the rights of African Americans.

_____

_____ **5.** Congress overrode President Johnson's veto of the Civil Rights Act of 1866.

_____

_____ **6.** The Fourteenth Amendment guaranteed citizenship and equal protection under the law to all people born or naturalized within the United States, without exception.

_____

_____ **7.** Although President Johnson was impeached for firing Secretary of War Edwin Stanton, the Senate failed to convict Johnson.

_____

_____ **8.** African American votes helped Ulysses S. Grant win the 1868 presidential election.

_____

_____ **9.** By 1870 all of the former Confederate states had rejoined the Union.

_____

_____ **10.** The Fifteenth Amendment gave women and African American men the right to vote.

_____

Name _____ Class _____ Date _____

Reconstruction

★ ★

DAILY QUIZ 20.3

MATCHING *10 points each* Match each of the following people or terms with the correct description by writing the letter of the description in the space provided. Some descriptions will not be used.

_____ **1.** carpetbaggers

_____ **2.** Tunis Campbell

_____ **3.** Ku Klux Klan

_____ **4.** Civil Rights Act of 1875

_____ **5.** Redeemers

_____ **6.** poll tax

_____ **7.** segregation

_____ **8.** Jim Crow laws

_____ **9.** *Plessy* v. *Ferguson*

_____ **10.** John Marshall Harlan

a. individuals behind the Democratic Party's return to power in the South at the end of Reconstruction

b. laws in southern states that required African Americans to stay in different hotels than whites, to sit in separate theater sections, and to ride in separate rail cars

c. northern-born Republicans who came South right after the war

d. name given to southern Republicans by southern Democrats because the Democrats considered them to be liars and cheats

e. Georgia justice of the peace who arrested white overseers who mistreated black workers

f. law that allowed African Americans to sue private businesses for discrimination

g. only Supreme Court justice who disagreed with the Court's ruling in *Plessy* v. *Ferguson*

h. person who was president of the United States at the time that Reconstruction ended

i. secret society whose purpose was to drive the Republicans out of the South and to deny African Americans equal rights

j. forced separation of whites and African Americans in public places

k. way in which Redeemers denied the vote to African Africans by requiring individuals to pay a special tax before they could vote

l. "separate-but-equal" argument that gave segregation the backing of the U.S. Supreme Court

★ ★

DAILY QUIZ 20.4

FILL IN THE BLANK *10 points each*   For each of the following statements, fill in the blank with the appropriate word, phrase, or name.

1. Because of the high cost of land and farm supplies, many African Americans became
_____ , people who farm land owned by someone else in exchange for the tools and supplies to farm.

2. Although _____ was one of the most important cash crops in the South, the fact that too many farmers planted it caused the supply to become too great and the price to drop.

3. Business leaders hoped the development of southern industries would strengthen the southern economy and create a "_____ ."

4. One of the great changes in the South after the Civil War was the growth of
_____ , which allowed companies to ship goods faster and farther than ever before.

5. When the cotton mill industry started, workers labored _____ days a week,
_____ hours a day.

6. The most famous writer about the South at the end of Reconstruction was probably Mark Twain, whose real name was _____ .

7. Joel Chandler Harris wrote many short stories about a fictional plantation slave named
_____ , a wise old storyteller who taught lessons by reciting folktales.

8. African American writer Charles W. Chesnutt showed the greed and cruelty of the slavery system in his book called _____ .

9. One of the most important musical styles of the time was the _____ , which was based on Christian hymns and African music sung in the days of slavery.

10. During Reconstruction, the _____ Singers were among the first people to bring African American music to a national audience.

★ ★

DAILY QUIZ 21.1

MATCHING *10 points each*   Match each of the following people or terms with the correct description by writing the letter of the description in the space provided. Some descriptions will not be used.

_____ **1.** Fort Laramie Treaty

_____ **2.** reservations

_____ **3.** Bureau of Indian Affairs

_____ **4.** Sand Creek Massacre

_____ **5.** William Tecumseh Sherman

_____ **6.** Treaty of Medicine Lodge

_____ **7.** Quanah Parker

_____ **8.** Sitting Bull

_____ **9.** Long Walk

_____ **10.** Massacre at Wounded Knee

a. former Civil War officer who threatened to exterminate all Sioux men, women, and children

b. Sioux leader who fled to Canada with a few of his followers

c. 1867 treaty in which most of the southern Plains Indians agreed to live on reservations, an agreement that brought the disapproval of many Comanche leaders

d. agency of the U.S. government that operated the Indian reservations

e. Montana trail used by miners, along which the U.S. Army built forts

f. first major treaty between northern Plains tribes and the U.S. government, signed in 1851

g. battle between Sioux Indians and troops led by General George Armstrong Custer that was the worst defeat the U.S. Army suffered in the West

h. battle between U.S. troops and Sioux in which at least 150 Indians died and that marked the end of more than 25 years of war on the Great Plains

i. last of the Comanche war leaders, who surrendered to the U.S. Army in 1875

j. areas of federal land set aside for American Indians

k. forced 300-mile march of Navajo captives to a reservation at Bosque Redondo, New Mexico

l. attack on Black Kettle's camp led by Colonel John M. Chivington that resulted in the death of around 200 men, women, and children

TRUE/FALSE *10 points each* Indicate whether each statement below is true or false by writing *T* or *F* in the space provided. If the statement is false, explain why.

_____ **1.** The prospectors who raced west to Pikes Peak were known as "fifty-niners."

_____

_____ **2.** The Comstock Lode, first thought to be a rich find, turned out to be worthless.

_____

_____ **3.** Mining became a big business run by large companies because few individuals could afford the equipment necessary to mine and refine ore.

_____

_____ **4.** Mining was one of the least hazardous jobs in the West.

_____

_____ **5.** Mining booms produced boom towns, which grew suddenly when a mine opened and disappeared just as suddenly when the mine closed down.

_____

_____ **6.** The creation of the Pony Express put the telegraph out of business.

_____

_____ **7.** To help railroad companies build a transcontinental railroad, the federal government abolished the Pacific Railway Acts in 1862.

_____

_____ **8.** The Central Pacific and Union Pacific Railroads met at Promontory, Utah, on May 10, 1869.

_____

_____ **9.** Railroad companies did not allow people to invest money in the railroads.

_____

_____ **10.** By 1890 railroads had become one of the biggest industries in the United States.

_____

FILL IN THE BLANK *10 points each* For each of the following statements, fill in the blank with the appropriate word, phrase, or name.

1. Spanish and English breeds of cattle brought to the West mixed, and by the 1800s had produced the Texas _____ .

2. In 1867 businessman _____ built cattle pens in Abilene, Kansas, so that cattle could be shipped by rail from Abilene directly to processing plants in St. Louis, Missouri.

3. The Cattle Kingdom stretched from _____ to Canada.

4. Western cowboys borrowed much from the Mexican _____ who had worked on ranches, including the western saddle, the lariat, and leather chaps.

5. _____ , long journeys where cowboys herded cattle to market or to the northern Plains for grazing, usually lasted several months and covered hundreds of miles.

6. The most heavily used route for moving cattle was the _____ , which headed north from San Antonio, Texas, to Dodge City, Kansas.

7. In 1882 _____ used the newly invented refrigerator railroad car to carry beef from packing plants to the big eastern cities, increasing the national demand for beef.

8. In 1873 Joseph Glidden invented _____ , which made it much easier to fence off large amounts of land at a low cost.

9. Competition for land on which to graze their cattle led to _____ between large ranchers, small ranchers, and farmers.

10. Cattle ranchers also fought with _____ owners, whose animals would chew the grass down to where it could no longer feed cattle.

★ ★

DAILY QUIZ 21.4

MULTIPLE CHOICE *10 points each* For each of the following, write the letter of the *best* choice in the space provided.

_____ **1.** The Homestead Act
   a. gave over 17 million acres of federal land to the states.
   b. made it more difficult for settlers to move to the West.
   c. gave government-owned land to small farmers.
   d. made it illegal in the West to build houses made of sod.

_____ **2.** Who encouraged people to move west by printing posters and pamphlets advertising fertile and inexpensive land?
   a. cattle ranchers
   b. sodbusters
   c. the U.S. government
   d. railroad companies

_____ **3.** One of the first things that many pioneer communities did was
   a. built a fort for protection.
   b. establish a local church and a school.
   c. build a grocery store and a saloon.
   d. elect a sheriff and build a jail.

_____ **4.** The people who introduced American farmers to a type of red wheat that grew very well on the Plains were the
   a. Comanche.
   b. Germans.
   c. Mennonites.
   d. Swedish.

_____ **5.** Settlers on the Plains found life difficult because
   a. the land was too rocky to grow any crops.
   b. weather conditions often were dangerous and unpredictable.
   c. the region had quickly became over-crowded and polluted.
   d. American Indians constantly waged war with them.

_____ **6.** The person who invented a deep steel plow that made it possible to break through sod on the Plains was
   a. Hardy Campbell.
   b. John Deere.
   c. Cyrus McCormick.
   d. Oliver Dalrymple.

_____ **7.** Dry farmers
   a. stopped planting red wheat, which needed too much rain, and started planting corn.
   b. irrigated their crops by hand.
   c. could find no way to make it through the drought years, so they left the Plains for eastern cities.
   d. left part of their fields unplanted each year so that the soil preserved water.

_____ **8.** Pioneer families on the Plains made their wash soap from
   a. lye and animal fat.
   b. crushed insects and cattle hooves.
   c. animal bones and wheat.
   d. sod and corn.

_____ **9.** Many pioneer women helped raise money for their families by
   a. selling farm machinery.
   b. taking cattle on cattle drives.
   c. raising chickens and making butter.
   d. letting railroad companies use their photographs in advertisements.

_____ **10.** Who were the Exodusters?
   a. African Americans who moved west in large numbers
   b. American Indians who helped settlers adapt to the western environment
   c. members of a religious group who came to the Great Plains from Russia
   d. government agents who helped farmers whose crops were destroyed

Name _____ Class _____ Date _____

★ ★ ★ ★ ★ ★ ★ ★ ★ ★ ★ ★ ★ ★ ★ ★ ★ ★ ★ ★

GEOGRAPHY AND HISTORY QUIZ

The Economy of the West

TRUE/FALSE *20 points each* Indicate whether each statement below is true or false by writing *T* or *F* in the space provided. If the statement is false, explain why.

_____ **1.** The majority of the gold and silver produced in the western United States came from the tireless efforts of individual prospectors.

_____

_____ **2.** Cattle trails ended at towns along railroad lines so that the cattle could easily be shipped to processing plants in the East.

_____

_____ **3.** Between 1880 and 1900, the number of miles of steel railroad lines in the United States grew from less than 100,000 to nearly 200,000.

_____

_____ **4.** Today farming accounts for the largest portion of the total annual U.S. gross national product.

_____

_____ **5.** During the late 1800s, immigration was an important contributor to population growth in the western United States.

_____

MATCHING *10 points each*   Match each of the following people or terms with the correct description by writing the letter of the description in the space provided. Some descriptions will not be used.

_____ **1.** Bessemer process

_____ **2.** patent

_____ **3.** Thomas Alva Edison

_____ **4.** Alexander Graham Bell

_____ **5.** Second Industrial Revolution

_____ **6.** free enterprise

_____ **7.** entrepreneurs

_____ **8.** vertical integration

_____ **9.** horizontal integration

_____ **10.** trust

a. Scottish-born professor who invented the "talking telegraph," or telephone

b. method by which several tons of iron could be made into steel in only 10 or 20 minutes instead of a day or more

c. owning businesses involved in each step of a manufacturing process

d. legal arrangement grouping a number of companies under a single board of directors

e. companies that sell shares of ownership called stocks

f. exclusive right to manufacture or sell an invention

g. business that is free from government involvement

h. Menlo Park inventor whose research team invented an electric lightbulb

i. person whose steel mills were by 1901 producing more steel than all the mills of Great Britain

j. period of explosive growth in U.S. manufacturing in the late 1800s

k. people who organize new businesses

l. owning all the businesses in a particular field

FILL IN THE BLANK *10 points each*   For each of the following statements, fill in the blank with the appropriate word, phrase, or name.

1. During the Second Industrial Revolution, _____ replaced many skilled workers.

2. Factories gradually came to focus on _____ —having workers repeatedly perform a single step in the production process—because it lowered costs and increased production.

3. Workers formed _____ , usually in spite of their employers' objections, to improve working conditions.

4. _____ involves union leaders negotiating for better wages and working conditions on behalf of all workers in a particular factory or industry.

5. Founded by a man named Uriah Stephens, the _____ was a union originally organized like a secret society.

6. During the _____ , more than 60 police officers were wounded, 8 police officers died, and 100 workers were wounded by police.

7. The American _____ organized individual national unions, such as the mineworkers and the steelworkers unions, into a loose association.

8. During the _____ Strike, Henry Frick locked workers out of the plant, and refused to negotiate with the union or allow union members back to work.

9. Workers at the _____ Palace Car Company went on strike in 1894 to protest wage cuts that occurred during a depression.

10. The _____ Act was used to break the strike of the Car Company workers and keep the trains rolling.

Name _____ Class _____ Date _____

An Industrial and Urban Nation

★ ★

DAILY QUIZ 22.3

MULTIPLE CHOICE *10 points each* For each of the following, write the letter of the *best* choice in the space provided.

_____ **1.** Old immigrants had come to the United States mainly from
    a. China, Korea, Vietnam, and Japan.
    b. Britain, France, Germany, and Italy.
    c. Britain, Germany, Ireland, and Scandinavia.
    d. Australia, Italy, and New Zealand.

_____ **2.** From where were most of the new immigrants from?
    a. southern and eastern Europe
    b. western Europe
    c. Asia and the Pacific
    d. Africa

_____ **3.** Most immigrants traveled to the United States
    a. in steerage aboard ocean-going ships.
    b. on barges over canals.
    c. aboard steamships over rivers.
    d. over land by locomotives.

_____ **4.** Which group of people did Congress in 1882 ban from immigrating to the United States for the next 10 years?
    a. Japanese people
    b. Chinese people
    c. Irish people
    d. German people

_____ **5.** Why did some immigrant communities form benevolent societies?
    a. to help immigrants apply to the U.S. government for aid benefits
    b. to help those immigrants who wanted to return to their home countries
    c. to help newly arrived immigrants find high-paying, skilled jobs
    d. to help other immigrants in cases of sickness, unemployment, and death

_____ **6.** The U.S. government used Ellis Island in New York Harbor as a(n)
    a. education center for immigrant children.
    b. processing center for newly arrived immigrants.
    c. housing center where new immigrants could live rent-free for one year.
    d. place where immigrants could come to learn English and U.S. history.

_____ **7.** The center of social and political life for urban African Americans was the
    a. benevolent society.
    b. church.
    c. school.
    d. city library.

_____ **8.** Who designed New York City's Central Park?
    a. Frederick Law Olmstead
    b. Jacob Riis
    c. Jane Addams
    d. Henry Blake Fuller

_____ **9.** Mass transit networks made it possible for many middle-class Americans to
    a. live in high-rise city apartments.
    b. live in the cities and work in the suburbs.
    c. live in the suburbs and work in the cities.
    d. move out of the cities and live in rural areas.

_____ **10.** The most famous settlement house in the United States was
    a. Addams House.
    b. Hull House.
    c. Locust Street Social Settlement.
    d. Central Park Settlement.

An Industrial and Urban Nation

★ ★ ★ ★ ★ ★ ★ ★ ★ ★ ★ ★ ★ ★ ★ ★ ★ ★ ★ ★

DAILY QUIZ 22.4

TRUE/FALSE *10 points each* Indicate whether each statement below is true or false by writing *T* or *F* in the space provided. If the statement is false, explain why.

_____ **1.** From 1860 to 1900, the U.S. population more than tripled, from 31 million to 100 million.

_____

_____ **2.** Because many farmers lost their farms and homes during the late 1800s, by 1880 one fourth of all farms were rented by tenants.

_____

_____ **3.** The National Grange was formed to improve farmers' living standards.

_____

_____ **4.** Congress created the Interstate Commerce Commission to provide uniform national regulations over trade between states.

_____

_____ **5.** The Coinage Act of 1873 placed the United States strictly on a gold standard.

_____

_____ **6.** Farmers supported coining silver to increase the money supply and raise prices.

_____

_____ **7.** The Greenback Party favored inflating the money supply with dollars backed by gold.

_____

_____ **8.** The Farmers' Alliance called for increased railroad regulation and lower interest rates.

_____

_____ **9.** The Populist Party wanted government ownership of railroads and telephone and telegraph systems, and supported free and unlimited coinage of silver and gold.

_____

_____ **10.** The 1896 election of William McKinley marked the end of the Populist Party.

_____

★ ★

DAILY QUIZ 23.1

FILL IN THE BLANK *10 points each* For each of the following statements, fill in the blank with the appropriate word, phrase, or name.

1. The striking contrasts between great wealth and poverty in the cities of the early 1900s caused people to refer to this period as the _____ Age.

2. The rapid growth of cities in the late 1800s made possible the rise of _____ , political leaders who controlled elections through bribery and payoffs.

3. In return for _____ and money, corrupt political leaders might provide jobs, order neighborhood improvements, or allow an illegal business to stay in operation.

4. Corrupt political leaders developed _____ , organizations that guaranteed votes at election time through both legal and illegal methods.

5. Through his corrupt practices, William Marcy _____ may have succeeded in stealing nearly $200 million from New York City's treasury.

6. During the presidency of _____ , members of his administration were jailed for taking bribes from whiskey distillers seeking to avoid paying taxes.

7. The _____ scandal damaged the careers of several politicians and led many Americans to question the honesty of the government and the presidency.

8. President _____ , a reformer, was assassinated at a Washington railroad station by a frustrated government job-seeker named Charles Guiteau.

9. Republican reformers, who came to be called _____ , left the Republican Party when a corrupt politician was chosen as the party's 1884 presidential nominee.

10. The _____ Act established a merit system for government jobs that was placed under the control of the Civil Service Commission.

Name _____ Class _____ Date _____

The Spirit of Reform

★ ★

DAILY QUIZ 23.2

MATCHING *10 points each*   Match each of the following people or terms with the correct description by writing the letter of the description in the space provided. Some descriptions will not be used.

_____**1.** progressives

_____**2.** muckrakers

_____**3.** Lincoln Steffens

_____**4.** Ida Tarbell

_____**5.** direct primary

_____**6.** Seventeenth Amendment

_____**7.** recall

_____**8.** initiative

_____**9.** referendum

_____**10.** John Dewey

a. constitutional amendment that outlawed slavery in the United States

b. political measure that allowed voters to choose candidates directly rather than relying on the choices of party leaders

c. group of reformers who began working in the late 1800s to improve society

d. political measure that ensured voter privacy

e. nickname given to journalists who raked up and exposed corruption in business and politics

f. journalist who wrote a series of articles describing the unfair business practices of the Standard Oil Company

g. constitutional amendment that allowed Americans to vote directly for U.S. senators

h. person who exposed scandals in city politics in the first muckraking article, published in 1902 in *McClure's Magazine*

i. political measure that allowed voters to approve or disapprove legislation already proposed by a state or local government

j. supporter of early childhood education who tried to develop teaching methods suited to the interests and needs of students

k. political measure that gave voters the ability to propose new laws by collecting a certain number of signatures on a petition

l. political measure that allowed the public to remove an elected official from office before the end of that person's term if enough voters signed a petition calling for the measure

CHAPTER

23

The Spirit of Reform

★ ★

DAILY QUIZ 23.3

TRUE/FALSE *10 points each*   Indicate whether each statement below is true or false by writing *T* or *F* in the space provided. If the statement is false, explain why.

_____ **1.** In 1900 more than 1.7 million children worked in mines, mills, and factories.

_____

_____ **2.** Jane Addams became the leader of the progressive crusade against child labor.

_____

_____ **3.** The Supreme Court declared federal child labor laws unconstitutional.

_____

_____ **4.** Progressives wanted to limit the number of hours in the workday to 12.

_____

_____ **5.** In 1902 Texas became the first of many states to adopt workers' compensation laws.

_____

_____ **6.** A fire in the Triangle Shirtwaist Factory in 1911 left 146 women dead.

_____

_____ **7.** In the 1908 case *Muller* v. *Oregon,* the Supreme Court overturned laws limiting the number of hours women could work.

_____

_____ **8.** In the system called capitalism, private businesses run most industries.

_____

_____ **9.** Under socialism, the government or workers own and operate the means of production.

_____

_____ **10.** The Industrial Workers of the World worked to bring all laborers together into one large industrial union that would work to overthrow capitalism and establish socialism.

_____

MULTIPLE CHOICE *10 points each* For each of the following, write the letter of the *best* choice in the space provided.

_____ **1.** Which of the following is *NOT* a women's college that was founded in the mid-1800s?
a. Vasser
b. Smith
c. Yale
d. Wellesley

_____ **2.** In 1910 the percentage of college students who were women rose to
a. 20 percent.
b. 40 percent.
c. 50 percent.
d. 60 percent.

_____ **3.** Many women of the Progressive Era became publicly active as members of
a. local government.
b. social clubs.
c. the court system.
d. male-dominated professions.

_____ **4.** The purpose of the Woman's Christian Temperance Union was to
a. encourage the spread of Christianity.
b. eliminate child labor.
c. work for world peace.
d. fight against alcohol.

_____ **5.** In his Atlanta Compromise speech, Booker T. Washington argued that African Americans should
a. focus on improving their own educational and economic well-being.
b. all move to the North.
c. fight violence with violence.
d. work to end discrimination and segregation around the world.

_____ **6.** In 1890 women gained full suffrage in
a. Wyoming.
b. New York.
c. Maryland.
d. Virginia.

_____ **7.** The Nineteenth Amendment, which gave American women the right to vote, was passed in
a. 1880.
b. 1900.
c. 1920.
d. 1940.

_____ **8.** Which of the following constitutional amendments outlawed the production and sale of alcoholic beverages?
a. Tenth Amendment
b. Fourteenth Amendment
c. Eighteenth Amendment
d. Twentieth Amendment

_____ **9.** The person who criticized Booker T. Washington for making African Americans responsible for correcting racial injustice was
a. John Dewey.
b. Jane Addams.
c. Frances Willard.
d. W. E. B. Du Bois.

_____ **10.** Which group of people did Congress in 1902 prohibit from immigrating to the United States for an indefinite period of time?
a. Mexican
b. German
c. African
d. Chinese

Name _____ Class _____ Date _____

★ ★

DAILY QUIZ 23.5

FILL IN THE BLANK *10 points each*   For each of the following statements, fill in the blank with the appropriate word, phrase, or name.

1. After the assassination of President _____ in 1901, Vice President Theodore Roosevelt took the oath of office.

2. President Roosevelt called his policy of balancing the interests of business, labor, and consumers the _____ .

3. During a coal miners' strike in 1902, President Roosevelt brought together the strikers and managers for _____ , a formal meeting to discuss and settle disagreements.

4. The most important goal of President Theodore Roosevelt's first administration was regulating _____ .

5. In 1906 the U.S. Congress passed the _____ Act, which prohibited the manufacture, sale, or transportation of mislabeled or contaminated food and drugs sold in interstate commerce.

6. President Roosevelt joined other progressives in the _____ movement, the effort to preserve nature and its resources.

7. After Roosevelt lost the 1912 Republican nomination to William Howard Taft, he and his followers formed the Progressive Party, which was nicknamed the _____ .

8. President Woodrow Wilson supported the _____ Act of 1913, which brought the lowest tariff rates the nation had seen in many years.

9. The Federal Reserve system, which was created in 1913 by the passage of the Federal Reserve Act, is made up of _____ regional Federal Reserve banks as well as many privately owned banks.

10. The _____ , established in 1914, investigated corporations and could issue restraining orders to prevent unfair trade practices.

★ ★

DAILY QUIZ 24.1

MATCHING *10 points each*   Match each of the following people or terms with the correct description by writing the letter of the description in the space provided. Some descriptions will not be used.

_____ **1.** imperialism

_____ **2.** isolationism

_____ **3.** William Seward

_____ **4.** Alaska

_____ **5.** McKinley Tariff

_____ **6.** Hawaii

_____ **7.** Matthew Perry

_____ **8.** spheres of influence

_____ **9.** Open Door Policy

_____ **10.** Boxer Rebellion

a. U.S. secretary of state who arranged the purchase of Alaska from Russia for $7.2 million

b. ruler of Hawaii who in 1893 announced a new constitution that returned power to the monarchy

c. areas where foreign nations control trade and natural resources

d. period of industrial and military modernization in Japan that began in 1868 and lasted for 40 years

e. territory whose acquisition added some 600,000 square miles to the United States, along with a wealth of natural resources

f. law that allowed all countries to ship sugar duty-free to the United States but gave U.S. sugar producers a subsidy of two cents per pound

g. commodore sent by President Millard Fillmore to Japan to deliver a letter suggesting a peaceful trade relationship between Japan and the United States

h. practice of extending a nation's power by gaining territories for a colonial empire

i. siege by Chinese nationalists angered by foreign involvement in Chinese affairs, mismanagement by the Chinese government, and the hunger and homelessness caused by a series of natural disasters

j. series of notes sent by Secretary of State John Hay to Japan and most European nations stating that all nations should have equal access to trade with China

k. area that became a U.S. territory in 1900 and the 50th state in the nation in 1959

l. avoiding involvement in the affairs of other nations

Name _____ Class _____ Date _____

DAILY QUIZ 24.2

TRUE/FALSE *10 points each* Indicate whether each statement below is true or false by writing *T* or *F* in the space provided. If the statement is false, explain why.

_____ **1.** In 1868 Puerto Ricans revolted against Spain, starting a decades-long struggle for freedom.

_____

_____ **2.** The United States began to prepare for war with Spain after the U.S. battleship *Maine* exploded and sank with a loss of 260 men.

_____

_____ **3.** After U.S. forces led by Commodore George Dewey destroyed Spain's Pacific fleet in the Philippines, U.S. troops and Filipino rebels took control of the capital, Manila.

_____

_____ **4.** The American soldiers known as Rough Riders came from many walks of life.

_____

_____ **5.** In the Battle of Santiago Bay every American ship was destroyed.

_____

_____ **6.** The treaty that ended the Spanish-American War placed Puerto Rico, Guam, Cuba, and the Philippines under Spanish control.

_____

_____ **7.** The Anti-Imperialist League accused the United States of building a colonial empire.

_____

_____ **8.** In 1946 the United States granted full independence to the Philippines.

_____

_____ **9.** The Platt Amendment gave Cuba the right to make treaties with other nations.

_____

_____ **10.** Puerto Ricans gained U.S. citizenship with the passage of the Jones Act in 1917.

_____

America As a World Power

★ ★

DAILY QUIZ 24.3

FILL IN THE BLANK *10 points each* For each of the following statements, fill in the blank with the appropriate word, phrase, or name.

1. In 1850 the United States and Great Britain had signed the _____ Treaty, which called for a partnership to build and maintain a canal.

2. After the Colombian senate rejected the Hay-Herrán Treaty, President Theodore Roosevelt considered other ways of gaining the _____ , such as seizing it by force.

3. With the signing of the Hay–Bunau-Varilla Treaty, the United States was finally ready to build the _____ Canal.

4. The first obstacle to overcome in building the canal was tropical disease, particularly _____ , which had proved to be a problem for the earlier French effort.

5. The dangers involved in building the canal, which opened to traffic on August 15, _____ , resulted in the loss of thousands of lives.

6. By issuing the _____ , President James Monroe warned European nations not to colonize or otherwise interfere in Central or South America.

7. In December 1904 President Theodore Roosevelt issued the _____ , which in effect placed the United States in the role of the Western Hemisphere's "police officer."

8. President William Howard Taft's approach to protecting U.S. interests in Latin America was called _____ and emphasized using U.S. economic power and business investment to influence Latin American governments.

9. President Woodrow Wilson rejected Taft's approach to Latin America and sought instead to protect U.S. interests in Latin America by encouraging the growth of _____ there.

10. Fearing renewed political unrest in the Dominican Republic, President Wilson in 1916 declared _____ on the island and established a government run by the U.S. Navy.

Name _____ Class _____ Date _____

America As a World Power

★ ★ ★ ★ ★ ★ ★ ★ ★ ★ ★ ★ ★ ★ ★ ★ ★ ★

DAILY QUIZ 24.4

MULTIPLE CHOICE *10 points each*   For each of the following, write the letter of the *best* choice in the space provided.

_____ **1.** Which of the following people ruled Mexico from 1877 to 1911?
  a. John S. Pershing
  b. Pancho Villa
  c. Emiliano Zapata
  d. Porfirio Díaz

_____ **2.** The biggest foreign investor in Mexico in the early 1900s was
  a. Spain.
  b. the United States.
  c. Great Britain.
  d. France.

_____ **3.** The Mexican Revolution was begun by democratic reformer
  a. Henry Mayo.
  b. Venustiano Carranza.
  c. Ciudad Juárez.
  d. Francisco Madero.

_____ **4.** How did President Woodrow Wilson respond when Victoriano Huerta assumed power in Mexico?
  a. He refused to recognize the new Mexican government.
  b. He offered to form an alliance with the new Mexican government.
  c. He offered Mexico a large loan to help rebuild its economy.
  d. He offered to establish a trade agreement between the two nations.

_____ **5.** The Mexican Revolution resulted in
  a. a large-scale Mexican migration to the United States.
  b. an end to diplomatic relations between Mexico and the United States.
  c. war between Mexico and the United States.
  d. a trade alliance between Mexico and the United States.

_____ **6.** Which of the following did *NOT* want the United States to intervene in Mexico?
  a. President Woodrow Wilson
  b. U.S. business leaders
  c. the domestic and foreign press
  d. members of Congress

_____ **7.** President Wilson asked Congress to approve the use of armed forces in Mexico after
  a. a U.S. ship patrolling in Mexican waters was bombed.
  b. U.S. sailors were arrested in Tampico, Mexico.
  c. Mexican ships attacked U.S. Navy ships in California waters.
  d. the Mexican president took over all U.S.–owned businesses in Mexico.

_____ **8.** Which countries tried to settle the dispute between the United States and Mexico?
  a. Canada, Britain, and Scotland
  b. Argentina, Brazil, and Chile
  c. Norway, Sweden, and Finland
  d. Haiti, Nicaragua, and Cuba

_____ **9.** Who became president of Mexico after Huerta was forced to leave office?
  a. Álvaro Obregón
  b. Emiliano Zapata
  c. Venustiano Carranza
  d. Santa Ysabel

_____ **10.** Pancho Villa, Emiliano Zapata, and Venustiano Carranza all
  a. wanted Mexico to become part of the United States.
  b. were at some time president of Mexico.
  c. wanted to overthrow Victoriano Huerta.
  d. were members of the ABC Powers.

Name _____ Class _____ Date _____

Modern America

★ ★ ★ ★ ★ ★ ★ ★ ★ ★ ★ ★ ★ ★ ★ ★ ★ ★ ★ ★

DAILY QUIZ E.1

MATCHING *10 points each*   Match each of the following people or terms with the correct description by writing the letter of the description in the space provided. Some descriptions will not be used.

_____ **1.** militarism

_____ **2.** Selective Service Act

_____ **3.** armistice

_____ **4.** Woodrow Wilson

_____ **5.** Treaty of Versailles

_____ **6.** Communists

_____ **7.** Eighteenth Amendment

_____ **8.** Jazz Age

_____ **9.** Harlem Renaissance

_____ **10.** Lost Generation

a. truce signed by Germany and the Allies on November 11, 1918, that ended World War I

b. people who believe that there should be no private ownership of property

c. name given to the group of writers who responded to the terrible death and destruction of World War I

d. U.S. president who proposed a plan called the Fourteen Points that outlined a system to avoid future wars

e. constitutional amendment that brought an end to prohibition

f. period of African American artistic accomplishment during the 1920s

g. U.S. president whose administration tried to concentrate on improving the economy of the 1920s but instead found itself weakened by scandal

h. constitutional amendment that banned the manufacture, distribution, and sale of alcohol in the United States

i. law passed by Congress during World War I requiring men between the ages of 18 and 45 to register for the draft

j. aggressive military preparedness combined with the belief that military force is a good solution to international problems

k. name given to the decade of the 1920s because many people liked to listen to a type of music that had its origins in African American culture

l. agreement by which Germany was to pay billions of dollars for the costs and damages of World War I

Modern America

★ ★

DAILY QUIZ E.2

FILL IN THE BLANK *10 points each*   For each of the following statements, fill in the blank with the appropriate word, phrase, or name.

1. On October 29, 1929, which became known as _____ , investors rushed to sell their stock, which caused already falling prices to drop even lower.

2. The severe global economic decline that had begun with the U.S. stock market crash is known as the _____ .

3. Some people charged that President _____ , who had been elected in 1928, acted too slowly to help the U.S. economy and the American people.

4. After Franklin D. Roosevelt was elected president in 1932, Congress passed a number of proposals that made up the _____ , Roosevelt's plan for improving the economy.

5. To reassure Americans that it was safe to return their money to the banks, Congress created the _____ Corporation, which insured people's bank deposits.

6. The most far-reaching legislation of the Roosevelt administration, the _____ Act, provided pensions for retired workers and unemployment insurance for workers who lost their jobs.

7. In the midst of the depression, a severe _____ hit the Great Plains, making it impossible for farmers to grow their crops.

8. Even though the United States maintained a policy of neutrality in the early part of World War II, Congress passed the _____ Act to allow the United States to lend or lease ships, planes, tanks, and guns to Britain.

9. On December 8, 1941, the United States declared war on Japan, one day after Japanese planes had bombed the U.S. naval base at _____ , Hawaii.

10. Around 6 million Jews and 3 million other people were killed by the Nazis during what is called the _____ .

Modern America

★ ★

DAILY QUIZ E.3

MULTIPLE CHOICE *10 points each*   For each of the following, write the letter of the *best* choice in the space provided.

_____ **1.** In the case *Brown* v. *Board of Education,* the Supreme Court declared that
  a. segregated schools were illegal.
  b. prayer in school was illegal.
  c. public schools must be made available to all students at no cost.
  d. school administrators had no right to censor school newspapers.

_____ **2.** The United Nations was created as
  a. an international law-enforcement organization.
  b. a military alliance of free nations.
  c. an organization for settling problems between countries.
  d. a trade alliance of wealthy nations.

_____ **3.** In response to the Soviet blockade of West Berlin,
  a. the western nations abandoned the city.
  b. the United States and Britain airlifted food and supplies there each day.
  c. all of the people in West Berlin moved to East Berlin.
  d. Britain and France declared war on the Soviet Union.

_____ **4.** The Cold War, a long power struggle for world influence, was fought by
  a. the United States and the Soviet Union.
  b. the United States and Germany.
  c. Germany and the Soviet Union.
  d. the Soviet Union and Japan.

_____ **5.** The policy stating that the United States would help any country struggling against communism was called the
  a. Warsaw Pact.
  b. Marshall Plan.
  c. North Atlantic Treaty Organization.
  d. Truman Doctrine.

_____ **6.** At the Potsdam Conference, Germany was divided into four zones, each to be controlled by one of the four main allies:
  a. Italy, Germany, France, and Britain.
  b. United States, China, Japan, and France.
  c. United States, Soviet Union, France, and Britain.
  d. Germany, Soviet Union, Japan, and Italy.

_____ **7.** The House Un-American Activities Committee investigated
  a. members of the House of Representatives suspected of accepting bribes for their votes.
  b. German citizens suspected of being Nazis during World War II.
  c. U.S. citizens who had helped the allies during World War II.
  d. U.S. citizens suspected of communist activities.

_____ **8.** Which nation did the United States compete against in the race for space exploration?
  a. France
  b. the Soviet Union
  c. Japan
  d. Britain

_____ **9.** The baby boom occurred after
  a. World War I.
  b. the Vietnam War.
  c. World War II.
  d. the Korean War.

_____ **10.** The leaders of which three nations met at the Yalta Conference in 1945?
  a. United States, Soviet Union, Britain
  b. Japan, Italy, Germany
  c. Germany, Italy, Soviet Union
  d. United States, France, Japan

Name _____ Class _____ Date _____

Modern America

★ ★

DAILY QUIZ E.4

TRUE/FALSE *10 points each*   Indicate whether each statement below is true or false by writing *T* or *F* in the space provided. If the statement is false, explain why.

_____ **1.** The most serious crisis faced by President Johnson was the Cuban missile crisis.

_____

_____ **2.** Great Society programs provided more Americans with health insurance, gave federal money to schools, and reduced the number of Americans living in poverty.

_____

_____ **3.** The Soviet Union was the first country to get a human on the moon.

_____

_____ **4.** In 1963, civil rights leaders organized the March of Washington to show their support for a new civil rights bill.

_____

_____ **5.** The Voting Rights Act of 1965 ensured every American's right to vote.

_____

_____ **6.** The Gulf of Tonkin Resolution gave President Lyndon Johnson the authority to remove all U.S. troops from Southeast Asia.

_____

_____ **7.** President Richard Nixon followed a policy of détente with the Soviet Union.

_____

_____ **8.** President Gerald Ford granted Richard Nixon a full pardon for his role in Watergate.

_____

_____ **9.** The Chicano movement worked to increase cultural pride among American Indians.

_____

_____ **10.** President Jimmy Carter negotiated a peace treaty between Israel and Egypt.

_____

Name _____ Class _____ Date _____

Modern America

★ ★

DAILY QUIZ E.5

MATCHING *10 points each*   Match each of the following people or terms with the correct description by writing the letter of the description in the space provided. Some descriptions will not be used.

_____**1.** supply-side economics   _____**6.** Operation Desert Storm

_____ **2.** Strategic Defense Initiative   _____**7.** Contract with America

_____ **3.** Ronald Reagan   _____**8.** Madeleine Albright

_____ **4.** George Bush   _____**9.** Internet

_____ **5.** Berlin Wall   _____**10.** Earth Summit

a. widely recognized symbol of communist rule that was torn down

b. U.S. president whose administration faced scandal over the Iran-contra affair

c. agreement that allowed goods, services, and people to move freely between the United States, Mexico, and Canada

d. first woman to be appointed U.S. secretary of state

e. expensive new space technology meant to protect the country from Soviet missiles

f. 10-point plan signed by Republicans promising a balanced budget, anticrime programs, welfare reform, and tax cuts

g. 1992 meeting of international delegates to discuss how to prevent global warming

h. global network tying together millions of computers

i. theory that lowering taxes will cause people to invest their savings in business and thus boost the economy

j. U.S. president who was nominated for the Nobel Peace Prize

k. military action taken by UN forces against Iraq for its invasion of Kuwait

l. U.S. president whose administration started the War on Drugs

ANSWER KEY

CHAPTER 1

QUIZ 1.1

1. b
2. c
3. b
4. b
5. a
6. c
7. c
8. a
9. d
10. d

QUIZ 1.2

1. environments
2. Aleut
3. bands
4. potlatches
5. California
6. desert
7. maize
8. mothers
9. wigwams
10. Iroquois

QUIZ 1.3

1. f
2. a
3. l
4. h
5. i
6. c
7. d
8. k
9. e
10. j

QUIZ 1.4

1. T
2. T
3. T
4. F; Kublai Khan opened trading networks with other countries.
5. T
6. T
7. F; West African kingdoms did participate in long-distance trading networks.
8. F; Most of Ghana's wealth came from trading gold.
9. T
10. T

CHAPTER 2

QUIZ 2.1

1. c
2. h
3. e
4. k
5. b
6. a
7. l
8. i
9. f
10. g

QUIZ 2.2

1. Asia
2. *Reconquista*
3. convert
4. *Santa María*
5. Taino
6. Line of Demarcation
7. Tordesillas
8. *La Navidad*
9. South America
10. Indians

QUIZ 2.3

1. F; The king chose Vasco da Gama for the expedition.
2. F; The fleet landed along the coast of present-day Brazil.
3. F; The voyage gave England a claim to land in North America.
4. T
5. T
6. F; He received funding from Spain.
7. T
8. T
9. F; Only one ship returned to Spain.
10. T

QUIZ 2.4

1. b
2. c
3. d
4. a
5. d
6. a
7. b
8. d
9. a
10. c

UNIT 1

GEOGRAPHY AND HISTORY QUIZ

1. Asia
2. Western
3. cow
4. corn
5. potato
6. cocoa
7. Asia
8. tomatoes
9. Great Plains
10. bee

CHAPTER 3

QUIZ 3.1

1. T
2. T
3. F; Once the ransom was delivered, Pizarro killed Atahuallpa.
4. F; He searched for gold and the Fountain of Youth in a land he named Florida.
5. T

6. T

7. F; He found adobe buildings and bushels of corn.

8. T

9. T

10. T

QUIZ 3.2

1. d	**6.** l
2. g	**7.** c
3. a	**8.** i
4. j	**9.** k
5. e	**10.** h

QUIZ 3.3

1. b	**6.** b
2. d	**7.** a
3. a	**8.** c
4. d	**9.** b
5. c	**10.** d

QUIZ 3.4

1. Florida	**6.** Dutch
2. Canada	**7.** Swedish
3. furs	**8.** Walter Raleigh
4. La Salle	**9.** Virginia Dare
5. Manhattan Island	**10.** Indians

CHAPTER 4

QUIZ 4.1

1. h	**6.** k
2. i	**7.** j
3. b	**8.** f
4. l	**9.** d
5. e	**10.** a

QUIZ 4.2

1. F; They wanted to reform the Church of England.

2. T

3. F; They moved to the Netherlands to escape persecution in England.

4. T

5. T

6. F; They invited the Wampanoag.

7. F; They were unhappy with its slow economic growth.

8. T

9. T

10. F; They had more rights.

QUIZ 4.3

1. dissenters	**6.** property
2. Great Migration	**7.** Bible
3. religion	**8.** Providence
4. town meeting	**9.** Anne Hutchinson
5. food	**10.** Salem

QUIZ 4.4

1. d	**6.** c
2. a	**7.** d
3. c	**8.** a
4. d	**9.** b
5. b	**10.** b

CHAPTER 5

QUIZ 5.1

1. T

2. F; They were proprietary, company, or royal.

3. F; The group was called the Privy Council.

4. T

5. F; Parliament is a two-house legislature.

6. T

7. F; The case established their right to freedom of the press.

8. T

9. F; It became known as the Glorious Revolution.

10. F; They declined significantly.

QUIZ 5.2

1. mercantilism	**6.** Middle Passage
2. balance of trade	**7.** profits
3. Navigation	**8.** diseases
4. Scotland	**9.** Quakers
5. triangular trade	**10.** Samuel Sewall

QUIZ 5.3

1. a	**6.** c
2. d	**7.** c
3. d	**8.** b
4. b	**9.** a
5. b	**10.** c

QUIZ 5.4

1. revivals	**6.** Presbyterian
2. Great Awakening	**7.** itinerant
3. Jonathan Edwards	**8.** childbirth
4. sinners	**9.** race
5. New Lights; Old Lights	**10.** political

QUIZ 5.5

1. f	**6.** b
2. d	**7.** c
3. j	**8.** k
4. a	**9.** i
5. l	**10.** g

UNIT 2

GEOGRAPHY AND HISTORY QUIZ

1. d	**6.** l
2. h	**7.** g
3. f	**8.** k
4. b	**9.** i
5. e	**10.** j

CHAPTER 6

QUIZ 6.1

1. F; Around 600 colonists and about 3,000 Indians died.
2. T
3. T
4. F; They rejected the plan.
5. F; It was the first battle.
6. T
7. T
8. F; The British capture of Quebec was a turning point in the war.
9. T
10. T

QUIZ 6.2

1. Atlantic	**6.** Pontiac
2. backcountry	**7.** Detroit
3. French and Indian	**8.** Proclamation of 1763
4. France	**9.** hated
5. Indian	**10.** Ohio River

QUIZ 6.3

1. g	**6.** d
2. c	**7.** k
3. l	**8.** f
4. i	**9.** e
5. j	**10.** b

QUIZ 6.4

1. c	**6.** c
2. d	**7.** c
3. b	**8.** d
4. b	**9.** b
5. a	**10.** a

UNIT 3

GEOGRAPHY AND HISTORY QUIZ

1. American Indians	**6.** married
2. slowed (or decreased)	**7.** British; Spanish
3. authority	**8.** Spain
4. enslaved Africans (or African Americans)	**9.** Canada
5. Virginia	**10.** Louisiana

CHAPTER 7

QUIZ 7.1

1. c	**6.** c
2. b	**7.** c
3. d	**8.** d
4. b	**9.** a
5. a	**10.** b

QUIZ 7.2

1. F; He argued that the colonies should break away from Britain.
2. T
3. F; The main argument was that countries should be ruled by laws made by the people.
4. T
5. F; They drew inspiration from Enlightenment writers, who argued that the people have the right to overthrow a corrupt government.
6. F; It created the United States of America.
7. T
8. T
9. F; Patriots favored independence; Loyalists remained loyal to Britain.
10. T

QUIZ 7.3

1. g	**6.** e
2. d	**7.** i
3. j	**8.** c
4. k	**9.** h
5. b	**10.** f

QUIZ 7.4

1. Saratoga
2. John Paul Jones
3. Trenton
4. supplies
5. Princeton
6. Marquis de Lafayette
7. Brandywine Creek
8. Bernardo de Gálvez
9. Kosciusko
10. Burgoyne

QUIZ 7.5

1. d
2. a
3. b
4. a
5. c
6. b
7. c
8. a
9. b
10. d

CHAPTER 8

QUIZ 8.1

1. b
2. i
3. e
4. l
5. g
6. a
7. k
8. c
9. h
10. j

QUIZ 8.2

1. Articles of Confederation
2. tariffs
3. Mississippi River
4. Britain
5. interstate commerce
6. money
7. debtors
8. depression
9. Shays's Rebellion
10. central

QUIZ 8.3

1. c
2. d
3. c
4. a
5. d
6. a
7. a
8. c
9. b
10. b

QUIZ 8.4

1. F; He urged them to sign it.
2. T
3. F; They were known as Antifederalists.
4. T
5. F; They were written by Alexander Hamilton, James Madison, and John jay.
6. F; It required the ratification of nine states.
7. T
8. T

9. T
10. F; The first 10 amendments make up the Bill of Rights.

UNIT 4

GEOGRAPHY AND HISTORY QUIZ

1. d
2. c
3. c
4. d
5. b
6. a
7. a
8. d
9. a
10. b

CHAPTER 9

QUIZ 9.1

1. b
2. h
3. d
4. f
5. j
6. a
7. k
8. g
9. c
10. i

QUIZ 9.2

1. T
2. F; The First Amendment prohibits government from supporting an official religion.
3. T
4. T
5. T
6. F; They protect the rights of accused persons.
7. T
8. T
9. F; This is a Sixth Amendment right.
10. T

QUIZ 9.3

1. naturalization
2. deport
3. president; vice president
4. laws
5. taxes
6. property taxes
7. jury duty
8. propaganda
9. political action committees
10. public interest

CHAPTER 10

QUIZ 10.1

1. George Washington
2. Motherhood
3. New York; Philadelphia
4. New York City
5. Thomas Jefferson
6. cabinet
7. Constitution
8. Judiciary Act
9. Supreme Court
10. John Jay

QUIZ 10.2

1. T
2. T
3. F; They disagreed on the issue.
4. T
5. F; He wanted to protect the powers of the states.
6. T
7. T
8. F; He believed in strict construction.
9. T
10. F; The bank provided stability and improved the economy.

QUIZ 10.3

1. b
2. d
3. c
4. c
5. a
6. b
7. d
8. c
9. a
10. b

QUIZ 10.4

1. Little Turtle
2. Fallen Timbers
3. Treaty of Greenville
4. Whiskey Rebellion
5. Alexander Hamilton
6. third
7. people
8. Farewell Address
9. borrow money
10. unity

QUIZ 10.5

1. h
2. c
3. f
4. j
5. g
6. b
7. i
8. a
9. l
10. k

CHAPTER 11

QUIZ 11.1

1. F; The Republican Party had won control of Congress from the Federalist Party.
2. T
3. T
4. F; He decreased military spending and repealed domestic taxes.
5. T
6. T
7. T
8. F; They disagreed about many things.
9. T
10. F; The Supreme Court gained a great deal of power.

QUIZ 11.2

1. d
2. a
3. d
4. b
5. b
6. c
7. a
8. c
9. a
10. b

QUIZ 11.3

1. Barbary
2. impressed
3. embargo
4. Non-Intercourse
5. Northwest Territory
6. Tecumseh
7. Tippecanoe
8. War Hawks
9. Federalists
10. James Madison

QUIZ 11.4

1. c
2. k
3. f
4. l
5. b
6. j
7. e
8. i
9. d
10. h

UNIT 5

GEOGRAPHY AND HISTORY QUIZ

1. F; It was bordered by Spanish-owned lands.
2. T
3. T
4. F; It established the border between the United States and Spanish territory.
5. F; Britain remained an important trading partner.

CHAPTER 12

QUIZ 12.1

1. British
2. Era of Good Feelings
3. Rush-Bagot Agreement
4. Convention of 1818
5. Seminole
6. Spain
7. Texas
8. Liberator
9. Mexico
10. Monroe Doctrine

QUIZ 12.2

1. T
2. F; It would allow Missouri to enter as a slave state and Maine to enter as a free state.
3. F; It remained a difficult issue.
4. F; It came to be known as the American System.
5. T
6. T
7. F; It was the Cumberland Road.
8. T
9. F; They all ran as Republicans.
10. T

QUIZ 12.3

1. h
2. e
3. c
4. a
5. l
6. b
7. g
8. j
9. i
10. k

QUIZ 12.4

1. b
2. a
3. a
4. c
5. d
6. c
7. c
8. d
9. a
10. b

QUIZ 12.5

1. Patrick Henry
2. Washington Irving
3. Rip Van Winkle
4. American Indians
5. historical fiction
6. *A New England Tale*
7. women
8. Hudson River school
9. Bingham
10. Greece; Rome

CHAPTER 13

QUIZ 13.1

1. f
2. c
3. h
4. l
5. d
6. a
7. k
8. e
9. j
10. g

QUIZ 13.2

1. b
2. c
3. a
4. a
5. d
6. c
7. b
8. c
9. a
10. d

QUIZ 13.3

1. Transportation Revolution
2. Robert Fulton
3. Hudson
4. Mississippi
5. clipper ship
6. Britain
7. Peter Cooper
8. Europe
9. 30,000
10. 20

QUIZ 13.4

1. T
2. T
3. T
4. F; They turned to steam power in stead of water power.
5. T
6. F; It was used to cut down wheat.
7. F; They made it possible to plant and harvest wheat fields.
8. T
9. T
10. T

CHAPTER 14

QUIZ 14.1

1. b
2. d
3. i
4. a
5. k
6. e
7. g
8. l
9. j
10. h

QUIZ 14.2

1. F; Great Britain was the South's main foreign trading partner.
2. T
3. T
4. F; The percentage is 14 percent.
5. F; Farmers also grew corn, sweet potatoes, wheat, and sugarcane.
6. T
7. T
8. F; They were built to process staple crops.
9. F; The lumber industry was important in the South.
10. T

QUIZ 14.3

1. b
2. b
3. d
4. a
5. c
6. a
7. b
8. c
9. d
10. c

QUIZ 14.4

1. fields
2. drivers
3. 10
4. property
5. cabins
6. codes
7. family
8. folktales
9. spirituals
10. Nat Turner

UNIT 6

GEOGRAPHY AND HISTORY QUIZ

1. b
2. d
3. c
4. b
5. b
6. d
7. b
8. d
9. a
10. a

CHAPTER 15

QUIZ 15.1

1. F; It was called the Second Great Awakening.
2. F; It appealed particularly to women.
3. T
4. F; It was written by Emerson.
5. T
6. T
7. T

8. F; It was written by Hawthorne.
9. T
10. T

QUIZ 15.2

1. Germany
2. potato
3. farmers
4. Protestants
5. nativists
6. Know-Nothing
7. manufacturing
8. middle class
9. tenements
10. cholera

QUIZ 15.3

1. b
2. a
3. d
4. c
5. c
6. d
7. a
8. b
9. d
10. a

QUIZ 15.4

1. e
2. g
3. c
4. b
5. l
6. a
7. j
8. f
9. i
10. k

QUIZ 15.5

1. abolition
2. Sarah Grimké
3. property
4. William Lloyd Garrison
5. Seneca Falls Convention
6. Declaration of Sentiments
7. 300
8. Lucy Stone
9. Susan B. Anthony
10. New York

CHAPTER 16

QUIZ 16.1

1. T
2. F; Most of the labor was done by American Indians living there.
3. F; They were known as Californios.
4. T
5. T
6. F; It was limited by the Comanche and the Apache living there.
7. T
8. T
9. T
10. T

QUIZ 16.2

1. b
2. f
3. h
4. e
5. a
6. l
7. d
8. j
9. c
10. k

QUIZ 16.3

1. Houston
2. annex
3. slave
4. Indians
5. land grants
6. Austin
7. free African Americans
8. Germany
9. land
10. Sam Houston

QUIZ 16.4

1. b
2. a
3. c
4. b
5. c
6. a
7. b
8. d
9. b
10. d

QUIZ 16.5

1. T
2. F; Of the original 87 members, 40 died.
3. F; He received permission from Mexican officials.
4. T
5. T
6. F; The U.S. government sent troops and money to ensure Indian cooperation.
7. T
8. T
9. T
10. F; The work of frontier artists became popular at the time in the East and in Europe.

CHAPTER 17

QUIZ 17.1

1. John C. Calhoun
2. Pacific Ocean
3. manifest destiny
4. American Indians
5. Texas
6. Britain
7. Oregon
8. Mexican
9. Nueces
10. James K. Polk

QUIZ 17.2

1. c
2. g
3. a
4. l
5. b
6. h
7. e
8. k
9. f
10. i

QUIZ 17.3

1. T
2. T
3. T
4. F; Laws were printed in both English and Spanish.
5. F; Place-names reflect the region's Mexican and Indian heritage.
6. F; The settlers used adobe.
7. T
8. T
9. T
10. F; Brigham Young chose present-day Utah.

QUIZ 17.4

1. c
2. a
3. d
4. a
5. c
6. a
7. c
8. b
9. a
10. b

UNIT 7

GEOGRAPHY AND HISTORY QUIZ

1. Texas
2. immigration
3. Britain
4. New Mexico
5. Hispanic
6. western
7. West
8. American Indians
9. Europe
10. Latin America

CHAPTER 18

QUIZ 18.1

1. k
2. d
3. g
4. i
5. b
6. c
7. h
8. f
9. e
10. j

QUIZ 18.2

1. T
2. T
3. F; They tried to get people to Kansas as quickly as possible.
4. F; Kansas had two governments.
5. T
6. T
7. F; A pro-slavery posse sent to arrest free-soilers sacked Lawrence.
8. T
9. F; It was Kansas.
10. T

QUIZ 18.3

1. Republican
2. Ostend Manifesto
3. Whig
4. slavery
5. Millard Fillmore
6. James Buchanan
7. Constitution
8. property
9. Lincoln-Douglas
10. Freeport Doctrine

QUIZ 18.4

1. b
2. a
3. d
4. a
5. d
6. c
7. c
8. b
9. b
10. a

CHAPTER 19

QUIZ 19.1

1. seven
2. Fort Sumter
3. Confederacy
4. Richmond
5. border states
6. West Virginia
7. Sanitary Commission
8. North
9. Mississippi
10. Washington

QUIZ 19.2

1. c
2. c
3. a
4. c
5. d
6. b
7. b
8. a
9. d
10. a

QUIZ 19.3

1. F; This was the Union strategy.
2. T
3. T
4. T
5. F; He failed to destroy the forts.
6. T
7. F; The Union laid siege to Vicksburg for six weeks and finally captured it.
8. T
9. T
10. F; The Indians fought on the side of the Confederates.

QUIZ 19.4

1. c
2. k
3. f
4. h
5. a
6. d
7. j
8. l
9. e
10. i

QUIZ 19.5

1. Cemetery Ridge
2. George Pickett
3. Union
4. Gettysburg Address
5. Ulysses S. Grant
6. William Tecumseh Sherman
7. Atlanta
8. total war
9. Appomattox Courthouse
10. treason

UNIT 8

GEOGRAPHY AND HISTORY QUIZ

1. T
2. T
3. F; This was a Union strategy.
4. T
5. F; Georgia saw the value of its farms cut in half.

CHAPTER 20

QUIZ 20.1

1. d
2. d
3. d
4. c
5. c
6. b
7. b
8. a
9. a
10. b

QUIZ 20.2

1. T
2. F; They were designed to help white southerners economically.
3. T
4. T
5. T
6. F; American Indians were excluded.
7. T
8. T
9. T
10. F; It gave African American men the right to vote.

QUIZ 20.3

1. c	6. k
2. e	7. j
3. i	8. b
4. f	9. l
5. a	10. g

QUIZ 20.4

1. sharecroppers	6. Samuel Clemens
2. cotton	7. Uncle Remus
3. New South	8. *The Conjure Woman*
4. railroads	9. spiritual
5. 6; 12	10. Fisk Jubilee

CHAPTER 21

QUIZ 21.1

1. f	6. c
2. j	7. i
3. d	8. b
4. l	9. k
5. a	10. h

QUIZ 21.2

1. T
2. F; It was a bonanza.
3. T
4. F; It was one of the most hazardous jobs in the West.
5. T
6. F; The telegraph put the Pony Express out of business.
7. F; The government passed the acts in 1862 and in 1864.
8. T

9. F; They encouraged people to invest money.
10. T

QUIZ 21.3

1. longhorn	6. Western Trail
2. Joseph McCoy	7. Gustavus Swift
3. Texas	8. barbed wire
4. vaqueros	9. range wars
5. Cattle drives	10. sheep

QUIZ 21.4

1. c	6. b
2. d	7. d
3. b	8. a
4. c	9. c
5. b	10. a

UNIT 9

GEOGRAPHY AND HISTORY QUIZ

1. F; The majority came from corporate mining operations.
2. T
3. T
4. F; Farming accounts for only 2 percent of the total U.S. annual gross national product.
5. T

CHAPTER 22

QUIZ 22.1

1. b	6. g
2. f	7. k
3. h	8. c
4. a	9. l
5. j	10. d

QUIZ 22.2

1. machines
2. specialization
3. labor unions
4. collective bargaining
5. Knights of Labor
6. Haymarket riot
7. Federation of Labor
8. Homestead
9. Pullman
10. Sherman Antitrust

QUIZ 22.3

1. c
2. a
3. a
4. b
5. d
6. b
7. b
8. a
9. c
10. b

QUIZ 22.4

1. F; It more than doubled, from 31.5 million to 70 million.
2. T
3. T
4. F; Congress passed the Interstate Commerce Act to provide uniform regulations over trade between states.
5. T
6. T
7. F; They favored paper dollars not backed by silver or gold.
8. T
9. T
10. T

CHAPTER 23

QUIZ 23.1

1. Gilded
2. bosses
3. votes
4. political machines
5. Tweed
6. Ulysses S. Grant
7. Crédit Mobilier
8. James Garfield
9. mugwumps
10. Pendelton Civil Service

QUIZ 23.2

1. c
2. e
3. h
4. f
5. b
6. g
7. l
8. k
9. i
10. j

QUIZ 23.3

1. T
2. F; It was Florence Kelley.
3. T
4. F; They wanted an 8-hour workday.

5. F; It was Maryland.
6. T
7. F; The Court upheld these laws.
8. T
9. T
10. T

QUIZ 23.4

1. c
2. b
3. b
4. d
5. a
6. a
7. c
8. c
9. d
10. d

QUIZ 23.5

1. William McKinley
2. Square Deal
3. arbitration
4. trusts
5. Pure Food and Drug
6. conservation
7. Bull Moose Party
8. Underwood Tariff
9. 12
10. Federal Trade Commission

CHAPTER 24

QUIZ 24.1

1. h
2. l
3. a
4. e
5. f
6. k
7. g
8. c
9. j
10. i

QUIZ 24.2

1. F; In 1868 Cubans revolted against Spanish rule.
2. T
3. T
4. T
5. F; Every Spanish ship was destroyed.
6. F; They were placed under U.S. control.
7. T
8. T
9. F; It limited Cuba's right to make treaties with other nations.
10. T

QUIZ 24.3

1. Clayton-Bulwer
2. Isthmus of Panama
3. Panama
4. yellow fever
5. 1914
6. Monroe Doctrine
7. Roosevelt Corollary
8. dollar diplomacy
9. democracy
10. martial law

QUIZ 24.4

1. d
2. b
3. d
4. a
5. a
6. a
7. b
8. b
9. c
10. c

EPILOGUE

QUIZ E.1

1. j
2. i
3. a
4. d
5. l
6. b
7. h
8. k
9. f
10. c

QUIZ E.2

1. Black Tuesday
2. Great Depression
3. Herbert Hoover
4. New Deal
5. Federal Deposit Insurance
6. Social Security
7. drought
8. Lend-Lease
9. Pearl Harbor
10. Holocaust

QUIZ E.3

1. a
2. c
3. b
4. a
5. d
6. c
7. d
8. b
9. c
10. a

QUIZ E.4

1. F; This crisis was faced by President Kennedy.
2. T
3. F; The United States was the first country to get a human on the moon.
4. T
5. T
6. F; It gave him the authority to take any measures necessary to secure peace in Southeast Asia.
7. T
8. T
9. F; It worked on behalf of Mexican Americans.
10. T

QUIZ E.5

1. i
2. e
3. b
4. l
5. a
6. k
7. f
8. d
9. h
10. g